UNWIN HYMAN
Short Stories
Collections
Plays

Series editor: Roy Blatchford
Advisers: Jane Leggett and Gervase Phinn

Unwin Hyman Short Stories
Openings   edited by Roy Blatchford
Round Two   edited by Roy Blatchford
School's OK   edited by Josie Karavasil and Roy Blatchford
Stepping Out   edited by Jane Leggett
That'll Be The Day   edited by Roy Blatchford
Sweet and Sour   edited by Gervase Phinn
It's Now or Never   edited by Jane Leggett and Roy Blatchford
Pigs Is Pigs   edited by Trevor Millum

Unwin Hyman Collections
Free As I Know   edited by Beverley Naidoo

Unwin Hyman Plays
Stage Write   edited by Gervase Phinn

CONTENTS   *Page*

*I*ntroduction

If pupils read plays they must be helped to realise that a play is not just words in the book but much more besides.

(The Newsom Report: Half Our Future)

The five plays in this collection are meant to be performed, interpreted and discussed. They are mere words on a page, unfulfilled, almost meaningless, until they are brought to life by actresses and actors colouring the words with voice and gesture, presenting the scenes on stage or on tape with sound effects and music.

These plays have been selected first and foremost because they are entertaining and thought-provoking. They are varied in themes and styles and should prompt students into considering questions which touch closely on their own lives, questions concerning child-parent conflicts, boy-girl relationships, individual freedom, rivalry, self-image, adolescent anxieties, friendship and other areas which are of concern and relevance to young people.

The first play in the collection, 'Home', is a sensitive and realistic exploration of the effects of divorce and separation on three people, Lisa, her father and step-mother, and is guaranteed to engage students in debate about their own feelings and experiences. The tensions which sometimes exist between parents and children is a theme pursued in 'Keep On Running', an original and thoroughly engrossing play which builds up to a powerful climax. This drama too should offer young readers the opportunity to enter into the kind of discussion which moves from the playtext into aspects of their own lives.

In Alma Cullen's engaging and skilfully constructed drama, 'The Audition', the central character is Rachel, a bewildering mixture of emotions and anxieties with whom many adolescents will identify.

'Replay For A Plumber' is a powerful and original play concerning two ordinary people caught up in some very extraordinary events.

Concluding the collection is 'Metamorphosid Arkwright'. It is an entertaining, refreshingly funny play with a robust action, a sharpness of characterisation and telling dialogue. Pupils will enjoy the punchy directness of the language.

Each play in this collection has its own special quality: one has a moving and melancholy atmosphere while another is uncompromising and challenging; one is lively and amusing, another disturbing and thought-provoking. All the plays should inspire students to consider and reflect on the various themes and should act as springboards for their own creative writing. All the writers include introductions which students should find helpful in understanding and appreciating their plays.

The Follow On activities at the end of the collection offer ideas for discussion, for writing and for further reading. They are particularly designed to meet the needs of the General Certificate of Secondary Education and to encourage students to respond to the plays in a wide variety of ways; through full class and small group discussion and through a series of writing assignments. They also offer a range of approaches for English and English Literature and Drama which will help students of all abilities, whether in building up a coursework folder or in preparing essays written under examination conditions. These activities aim to encourage students to:

— work independently and collaboratively
— consider:
>   the variety of plays: stage, radio, television, plays for voices
>   the language and style of the playwrights
>   the structure and development of the scenes
>   the development of character
>   the settings
>   the use of lighting, sound effects, music, costume, properties and stage sets

— examine the playwrights' viewpoints and intentions
— respond critically and imaginatively to the plays, orally and in writing
— read a variety of texts
— read more widely.

GERVASE PHINN

*H*ome

Ask anyone where their favourite place is, and they'll probably say home; yet home is a different place for all of us and is associated with all kinds of deeply personal memories and expectations. This interests me: home is a focus for raw drama.

When Lisa thinks she's going home she enters it as an outsider. It has become someone else's territory, and can never again be the home of her memory. The hopeless situation in which the three characters find themselves stems from the fact that all three have a right to this home, and yet their relationships can only be a painful one unless they can find a way of communicating. I needed a way of identifying the audience with Lisa, and the unposted letters became a vehicle for her real thoughts, but I also wanted you to be trapped in Alan's dilemma, and to sympathise with Claire. The situation is a familiar one, and can never be black and white.

I knew a girl whose situation was similar to Lisa's, and who found it so hard to talk to either of her parents about it and her unhappiness that her whole personality seemed to change; she became sullen and introverted, as if she couldn't trust herself to laugh any more, and she found it hard even to talk to people of her own age. She's now a self-possessed young woman running her own home and family, but to my knowledge she's never been able to tell her parents what she went through. It was nobody's fault, just circumstances beyond anyone's control, and she was helpless in the middle of it, and I was an outsider looking on. Often when I write about a teenage character I come to a point where they find talking to a parent difficult. It's a conflict we all face at some time, as children and as parents;

*we're growing away from each other and suddenly
something that was easily shared becomes too trivial or
painful to talk about. The longer we leave it the harder
it gets. I suppose it's a way of shaking loose the bonds
that have been too tight, but sometimes the bonds are
broken for ever. I think that's one of the saddest things
that can happen.*

BERLIE DOHERTY

CHARACTERS

LISA   sixteen years old
ALAN   Lisa's father
CLAIRE   Alan's second wife

*This play was commissioned for and performed on
Radio Sheffield.*

(*In a train*)

LISA Dear Dad,

I've got some wonderful news. I'm coming home. Mum has agreed to let me come and live with you now I've left school. I still can't believe it. I can come, can't I? I'm sure I'll be able to get a job to help pay for my keep. Please say I can come.

Love, Lisa.

ALAN Dear Lisa,

Claire and I are delighted that you're coming to live with us. I've written to your mother to make arrangements. Come as soon as you like.

Love, Dad.

(*Bring up train, and cross-fade into quiet, classical background music.*)

CLAIRE Right, Alan. I've moved all my stuff out of the spare room. It's all ready for painting now.

ALAN Are you sure you wouldn't like me to do it, Claire?

CLAIRE No. I'll do it. I know exactly how that room should look. I'd like to do it for her.

ALAN I'm sorry you've lost your studio space.

CLAIRE Look — we've talked about it enough. I've said yes, and I mean yes. I can't get on with painting these days anyway, not while Jamie's so small. It's Lisa's room now.

ALAN Thank you, Claire. Have a rest now. I'll get you some coffee.

(*Claire calls through to the kitchen.*)

CLAIRE I do hope Lisa will be happy with us, Alan.

ALAN Why shouldn't she be?

CLAIRE I don't think it's going to be easy for her.

ALAN It's not exactly going to be easy for any of us. Don't look for trouble... She's set her heart on moving in with me. It's what she's always wanted, you know...to come back here.

CLAIRE That's what I'm worried about.

(*Alan comes back in.*)

ALAN Here. Coffee and flapjack. I've been busy too, while you've been banging about up there.

10

CLAIRE   She's going to find a lot of changes here.

ALAN   Well, of course she is. She was only a little girl when her mother first moved out with her. Six or so. I don't think this house was ever home to her, in that sense.

CLAIRE   And there's the baby. She's not just coming back to her dad, she's coming back to a family.

ALAN   And she's part of it.

CLAIRE   I know, love..I didn't mean that.

ALAN   She is my family.

CLAIRE   I just hope it works out.

ALAN   You want her to come, don't you?

CLAIRE   Of course. Of course I do, Alan.

ALAN   And I want her to come, and she wants to come. It's going to be all right.
         (*Fade down music, bring up train.*)

CLAIRE   Dear Lisa,
         I thought I'd just drop you a line to say how delighted I am that you're coming to live with us. I'm doing up your room for you. I hope you like the colour scheme. I'm really looking forward to having you here....
         (*Lisa takes up the reading.*)

LISA   ....you'll be able to help with Jamie, which will be marvellous. Your dad is hopeless with babies! It'll be like having a younger sister in the house.
         Come soon.
         (*Claire takes up reading again.*)

CLAIRE   ..like having a younger sister in the house.
         Come soon.
         Love, Claire.
         (*Fade up train and cross-fade into background classical music.*)

ALAN   ...After all, Lisa's nearly the same age as you.

CLAIRE   I must be eight years older than her. That's a lifetime to a girl of Lisa's age. We can't be friends, Alan. It's not going to work that way.

ALAN   Make it work. She's not had an easy time with her mother.

11

CLAIRE	I suppose you feel guilty about that.
ALAN	Of course I do. You don't do things like that lightly. Dot's never forgiven me for divorcing her.
CLAIRE	For marrying me, you mean. Nearly half her age.
ALAN	Well, it didn't help, but you were what you might call a recent aggravation. She was bitter about it long before you came on the scene.
CLAIRE	She was the one who went away.
ALAN	She went away because she couldn't live with me any more. A long time ago.
CLAIRE	Did you ever try to make it up…?
ALAN	No. Never.
CLAIRE	So you were bitter too.
ALAN	I told you. You don't do these things easily. Anyway. Poor little Lisa. It wasn't her fault, poor kid. It was nothing to do with her.
CLAIRE	Well, she's got what she wants, now. Home to her Dad.
ALAN	And a nice new family. She'll be all right.

(*Fade down music, fade up train, and out. Front door opens.*)

ALAN	Well Lisa…here it is. Welcome home!
LISA	Thanks Dad.
ALAN	It's changed a bit since you were last here. Like it?
LISA	Bit trendy…
ALAN	Trendy!
LISA	Not quite what I'd expect for a balding old bear with middle-age spread…
ALAN	Enough of that and Claire's anything but a balding old bear, I'd have you know..and she's the one who does it all. That's one of the perks of being married to an artist. I can always rely on her taste.
LISA	The taste is in the mouth.
ALAN	What's that supposed to mean?
LISA	We like soft colours…greys and oatmeals. I thought you did.
ALAN	I did. I've learnt to be exciting.
LISA	Good for you! Where is Claire, anyway?
ALAN	Probably feeding Jamie. It seems to be her favourite

hobby.

LISA   What's he like Dad? I'm dying to see him. Is he anything like me?

ALAN   Not in the slightest. He's much better-looking. There — you deserved that for the blow you've just given me about my waistline and my taste.

LISA   Sorry Dad.

ALAN   He's got your lungs though! You should hear him at six in the morning. Well, you will of course. That's a treat in store for you.

LISA   D'you want me to get up and bring you breakfast in bed then?

ALAN   I remember your breakfasts in bed! Half a bowl of sugar with milk and a few cornflakes thrown in!

LISA   Yes. I remember. And I used to spill half of it coming up the stairs..tripping over my nightie!

CLAIRE   Lisa!

LISA   Hello.

ALAN   As you've gathered....Lisa, this is Claire. Claire... this is my big girl...Lisa.

CLAIRE   How lovely to meet you at last. I'm sorry I've been so long up there...Jamie's a pain, he really is. I think he's teething actually. But sit down, love. You do look nice. I love your jacket.

LISA   Thanks. St. John's market.

CLAIRE   Well, I'd never have guessed. And isn't her hair lovely, Alan?

LISA   I've just had it tinted.

ALAN   She looks like a red cabbage to me.

LISA   Mum hates it.

CLAIRE   Does she? Well, you know what mums are like. I think it suits you. It really does. I wouldn't mind a style like that myself. Mind you...you have to have a really young face to wear your hair like that.

ALAN   Well. It's good to have you home at last, Lisa.

CLAIRE   Yes. It is. It's lovely. I feel as if I've got a sister in the house now.

ALAN   I'll take your bags up to your room now, shall I?

LISA   You don't have to Dad. I know the way.

CLAIRE   I'll take her up. You dish up the food.

LISA   Can I see Jamie?

CLAIRE   Later. I've just put him down. Bring your bags up, will you?

(Fade upstairs. They're whispering.)

CLAIRE   The bathroom's at the end there.

LISA   I know…and this is my room.

(Opens door)

CLAIRE   Ssh! No. This is Jamie's room. Yours is that one.

LISA   I thought Dad would have remembered.

CLAIRE   What's the matter?

LISA   This was my room.

CLAIRE   Let me just close this door. That's better. He's a devil if he wakes up at this time. This is yours. Look. D'you like it?

LISA   Thanks.

CLAIRE   You do like it, don't you? I love strong colours like this.

LISA   I've noticed.

CLAIRE   I don't suppose it's everybody's taste.

LISA   It's lovely. I've brought some posters anyway.

CLAIRE   What for?

LISA   My posters. From home. Mum's.

CLAIRE   It's newly papered, Lisa. Don't spoil it.

ALAN   Dinner!

LISA   All right.

CLAIRE   Still…it's your room. You do what you want, love. Of course you must.

ALAN   Come on girls! It's ready!

CLAIRE   Listen to him! He'll have that baby awake! He never thinks, your dad…

(Fade. They're eating.)

ALAN   Another helping, Lisa? Go on, you finish it.

LISA   No thanks Dad. I've had enough.

CLAIRE   I expect she's on a diet. *(awkwardly)* Well…I always was, at your age.

LISA   I've had enough.

ALAN   You'd better not be on a diet. I've got some new stodgy recipes to try out on you.

CLAIRE Didn't know your dad could cook, did you Lisa?

ALAN Oh, she does. She used to come up here for her Saturday tea until they moved right out of Leeds. You remember those Saturdays, don't you Lisa? We used to spend the afternoon in the park, and then come back here for tea. You used to enjoy those Saturdays, didn't you?

CLAIRE What did he used to cook for you in those days, Lisa? Beans on toast?

LISA I can't remember.

ALAN I hadn't learnt to be exciting then.

CLAIRE She likes her bedroom, don't you Lisa?

ALAN Good.

LISA I thought I'd be having my old room, Dad.

CLAIRE Jamie's room. It's nice and warm for him in there.

LISA I loved that room.

CLAIRE (*awkwardly*) Well. We can't sit here all night. Perhaps you could wash up, Lisa, while I make some coffee. Then you two could walk down to the park...for old time's sake.
(*Fade to park.*)

ALAN How's your mother?

LISA She's all right.

ALAN What does she think about this...you coming here?

LISA Couldn't stop me, could she?

ALAN That's not what I asked you. What does she think about it?

LISA It's nothing to do with her, is it? Now, anyway.

ALAN So she wasn't too keen.

LISA Dad! It doesn't matter, does it. It's my choice.

ALAN Yes. It does matter.

LISA What about Claire? Does she mind?

ALAN Mind? Good Heavens, no! Why should she?

LISA She does though. I hate this place.

ALAN Mm?

LISA This park. I always hated it. You must have known that!
(*Fade park.*)

LISA Dear Dad,

15

I'm not going to send you this letter, but I want to write it anyway. I want to tell you that this has been the worst week of my life. Claire never talks to me, Dad. She's so nice to me when you're here, but when you're not...I wish you knew....
(*Pop music*)

CLAIRE   Lisa! Lisa! Turn it down, will you?

LISA   Sorry.

CLAIRE   The baby! And I'm trying to do some work.

LISA   Sorry. What are you doing?

CLAIRE   I'm trying to paint.

LISA   What's it supposed to be, though? I can't make it out.

CLAIRE   Lisa, I don't like to talk when I'm working.

LISA   Sorry.

CLAIRE   And stop saying.... Isn't there something you can do?

LISA   Like what?

CLAIRE   Never mind.

LISA   What time will Dad be back?

CLAIRE   Don't know.

LISA   Shall I take Jamie out for a walk?

CLAIRE   No. Let him sleep. Don't poke him, let him sleep.

LISA   D'you think he looks like me? Claire, d'you think he does?

CLAIRE   No.

LISA   My Dad's taking me out for a drink tonight.

CLAIRE   Tonight?

LISA   I'm old enough.

CLAIRE   He's forgotten. We've got a dinner date with some friends.

LISA   So I'm baby-sitting.

CLAIRE   Not if you don't want to.
(*Lisa hums to the record player.*)

CLAIRE   Lisa. Please!

LISA   Sorry.

CLAIRE   I wish you'd do something. Go and read.

LISA   I haven't got a book.
(*She goes.*)

CLAIRE   Then write one!

(Slammed door wakes baby up. Later. Kitchen sounds.)

ALAN   Hello love!

CLAIRE   Alan…you haven't forgotten we're going out tonight, have you?

ALAN   Andy and Mary's? No, course not.

CLAIRE   Lisa thinks she's going out with you.

ALAN   I'll take her out tomorrow instead. OK? Where is she?

CLAIRE   In her room, probably.

ALAN   At this time of day?

CLAIRE   She should spend more time up there.

ALAN   Why should she?

CLAIRE   Teenagers always like to stay in their own rooms. I did. She could have a record-player up there, couldn't she?

ALAN   Has she asked you for one?

CLAIRE   She hasn't asked me for anything. I just think it would be nice for her…

(Fade. Knock on Lisa's door.)

ALAN   Can I come in?

(She's been crying.)

LISA   Oh…Dad. All right.

ALAN   What are you doing up here, sitting in the dark on your own?

LISA   Nothing. I was having a sleep.

ALAN   Let's have a look at you…

Oh, Lisa love. What's this about, eh?

LISA   Nothing.

ALAN   What's up?

LISA   I never see you…

ALAN   I have to go to work.

LISA   At night. I mean. You're going out again tonight.

ALAN   Claire likes to be taken out. And I like to see my friends…

LISA   I see.

ALAN   Are these all your records? Claire was saying that you might like a record-player.

LISA   There's your stereo.

ALAN   No…in here, I mean. Would you like to have your

	own record-player up here in your own room?
Lisa	There's no need.
Alan	Only if you want it.
Lisa	So she can get on with her painting?
Alan	Well...maybe. Maybe you both need to be on your own sometimes.
Lisa	I'm in the way, aren't I?
Alan	I didn't say that.
Lisa	She did though, I bet.
Alan	Lisa, what is this?
Lisa	I look after Jamie for her, don't I?
Alan	I know. And she's very grateful, of course she is.
Lisa	That gives her a chance to get on with her painting.
Alan	It means a lot to her.
Lisa	She's not very good though, is she?
Alan	I don't know.
Lisa	I don't think she is.
Alan	I wish you wouldn't be so difficult, Lisa.
Lisa	Dad. Before I came ...did Claire use this room?
Alan	As a studio? Now and then, yes.
Lisa	I wish you'd told me that. There isn't really room for me here, is there?
Alan	Of course there is. We've had to do a bit of adjusting, that's all. Things will be easier when you get a job or a course of some sort. But don't sit up here crying. If you're unhappy, tell me. I'm still your old dad, remember.
	(*Fade.*)
Lisa	Dear Dad,
	How can I tell you? I wish I'd never come back here. It's different. You're different. It's all I ever wanted, to come back home to you. And now I've come, and it's too late. That's what I'd tell you. You're not my old dad anymore. You're her husband.
	Lisa.
	(*Baby crying, television on.*)
Claire	Alan, I've had as much of this as I can take.
Alan	I'll see to him.
Claire	Lisa, I'm talking about. You ought to see her when

18

you're not here. She's like a ghost, the way she walks round the house all day. Or she just sits in that chair, staring into space. She won't talk to me...she just shrugs when I speak to her. She won't do a thing to help round the house unless I ask her to. She has that awful music of hers on at top volume and if I ask her to turn it down she sulks. I can't work with her in the house.

ALAN   You're being a bit hard on her. She hasn't much confidence in herself. You're not helping.

CLAIRE   I've done my best. I've given up, that's all. It's been weeks now...months. How much longer?

ALAN   For good, and you know it. For as long as Lisa needs a home.

CLAIRE   I didn't know how hard it was going to be.

ALAN   It's hard for all of us.

CLAIRE   She's not my daughter!

ALAN   There's one solution, I suppose, if you don't like being in the house together all day.

CLAIRE   What's that?

ALAN   Lisa can't seem to get a job...d'you think you could go back to yours?

CLAIRE   Why should I? I don't want to!

ALAN   She could look after Jamie. That could be her job. We could pay her to do that.

CLAIRE   That's my job! I want to be at home with my baby!

ALAN   Try it.

CLAIRE   I won't try it. I'm not getting out of my house so your lazy daughter can lounge round in it all day. I want to be at home. That's all I want at the moment — my home, and my baby, and you. I think I've a right to that.

ALAN   Lisa has a right to a home as well.

CLAIRE   It's not our home anymore.

ALAN   Ssh! Shush now Claire...

CLAIRE   Not like it used to be. Is it never, never going to be like that again?

   (*Cut to....*)

LISA   Sometimes I hear you both in your bedroom. I can't

help hearing you. I hate it. I hate to hear you doing it to her.

(*Cut to....*)

CLAIRE   Lisa! Are you going out?

LISA   Yes. I'm just going down to the job centre. Why? Have I to do the shopping again?

CLAIRE   No, I'm going out too. I thought I might walk down with you, that's all.

(*Outside*)

CLAIRE   Have you been in touch with your Mum recently?

LISA   No.

CLAIRE   Oh, Lisa, you must write to her. She'll be missing you.

LISA   No she won't.

CLAIRE   I'm sure she will. Mothers do, you know.

LISA   She couldn't wait to get rid of me.

CLAIRE   What makes you say that?

LISA   She's got a new boyfriend, hasn't she? She wanted the place to herself.

CLAIRE   I didn't know. Does Alan know?

LISA   What's it got to do with him? D'you think he'd be jealous or something?

CLAIRE   Course not. Why should he?

LISA   She hates him, d'you know that? It doesn't make sense to me. How could anyone hate my Dad? She used to love him, and now she hates him. I can't understand that.

CLAIRE   You will, Lisa.

(*Fade.*)

ALAN   Claire. Where's Lisa?

CLAIRE   Upstairs. In bed, I think.

ALAN   I think I might have found the answer. I know how much you resent giving up your privacy...and I agree, I've been unfair to you. It's unreasonable of me to expect you to sacrifice so much.

CLAIRE   I thought I was the one who was being unreasonable.

ALAN   Don't start that again. This is what I was thinking Claire...maybe we could find a room somewhere.

CLAIRE   A room?

ALAN	It might be the answer. Somewhere cheap…not too far away.
CLAIRE	We've both had the same idea then. And there is one. I had a look in the papershop window. It's the launderette — just round the corner.
ALAN	There you are then. If you could get that, you could pop down there when you feel like it…just for an hour or so.
CLAIRE	I could?
ALAN	It's never been satisfactory for you, having to clear away your painting things every day, having interruptions from Jamie…If they'd let you take that room as a studio you could go there for as long as you liked.
CLAIRE	I can't believe what you're saying. There's a perfectly good room in my own house for me to use as a studio.
ALAN	Ssh!
CLAIRE	And your daughter's sleeping in it!
ALAN	All right. Forget it. Forget about the room.
CLAIRE	No. Don't forget about the room. It's an excellent idea, nearly the same as mine of course, but not as obvious. It's a bedsit actually, and I suggest we get it for Lisa.
ALAN	It's unthinkable.
CLAIRE	Why is it unthinkable?
ALAN	She's too young.
CLAIRE	I left home at her age.
ALAN	You went to college. No, Claire, forget about it. She's staying here.
CLAIRE	Isn't that for us both to decide?
ALAN	She's my daughter. I want her here.
CLAIRE	Perhaps you should have thought of that before you and Dot split up. I married you, not your lazy lump of a daughter.
ALAN	Shut up! She'll hear you.
CLAIRE	I don't care if she does hear me. In fact I think she should be brought into this conversation, so she knows exactly where she stands.
ALAN	Not while you're in this mood. She's only a kid, when

all's said and done. You have to make allowances for her. Give her time.

CLAIRE As far as I'm concerned, her time is up. Or ours. D'you know what she said about Dot? She said she used to love you, and now she hates you. It happens. Fancy it happening to someone like you. Fancy it happening to us.

ALAN Claire. Don't.

CLAIRE I'm going out to have a look at that bedsit. And if she's not prepared to move into it, then I will.
(*She goes out. Baby starts crying.*)

ALAN Oh God!

LISA Dear Dad,
I can hear you and Claire rowing downstairs. About me. Again.
It's not my fault, is it? I've tried to fit in, dad. It's not her fault either, I suppose. She didn't choose me, and I didn't choose her. You see, I do understand.
(*Door opens.*)

ALAN See to Jamie, will you Lisa? I'm going out for a bit.

LISA Where's Claire?

ALAN She's gone out. She's a bit upset.

LISA What are you going to do, dad?

ALAN I thought I'd try and find her and take her out for a drink.

LISA Talk to her, I suppose?

ALAN Yes.

LISA Of course.

ALAN Of course what?

LISA Nothing. Have a nice time.

ALAN He's started up again.

LISA Don't worry. I can see to Jamie.

ALAN You don't mind baby-sitting?

LISA Oh no, I don't mind baby-sitting. After all, he's my brother, isn't he?
(*Fade. Jamie is crying.*)

LISA Don't start again Jamie. Come on little one. There's a good boy. Ssh now! Oh, shussh. What am I going to do, eh, Jamie? Don't look at me like that. You know all the answers, wise old thing. You're the one I can talk to here. I want to be with my dad, that's all. That's not much to want, is it Jamie? I wish it was just him and me. I wish it was just him and me and my Mum again. In this house.

I bet you wish it was just you and your mum and dad again, don't you? Not rowing. I bet Claire does. Loving before the hating starts, all over again.

Don't start again. What've you got to cry about? No one's going to chuck you out. No one's going to pinch your dad off you. Shush baby. Shush, will you?

Shut up. Shut up. Bloody, bloody baby. Shut up! (*Crying intensifies and stops abruptly. Cut to Claire and Alan walking home.*)

ALAN   Feeling better now?

CLAIRE   Mmm. Fine. It's a lovely night, Alan. Look at those stars. We should sleep out under the stars, nights like this.

ALAN   Romantics like you get rheumatism.

CLAIRE   You're an old fogey at heart, you know. I don't know what I see in you. I should have dragged you away by your hair long ago, away from this suburban little house with its cardboard walls.

ALAN   You did, Claire. You dragged me away from myself.

CLAIRE   You thought everyone hated you.

ALAN   Dot did. That seemed like everyone to me.

CLAIRE   We mustn't let things go wrong again, out of hand, like this. I love you too much.

ALAN   Claire. We nearly lost each other.

CLAIRE   We'll be all right now.

ALAN   New start.

CLAIRE   New start. Promise.

ALAN   And a new start with Lisa. I'll take her for a drink tomorrow.

CLAIRE   That's all she needs you know. More time with her dad.

ALAN   It'll be all right now.
          (*Key in door. Baby crying in distance.*)

CLAIRE   Listen to him! This is what she does, Alan. She just ignores him.

ALAN   Now, what did we say...?

CLAIRE   She tries my patience though, she really does.

ALAN   You see to him. I'll get some supper ready. I'll see if Lisa wants some.

(In the front room.)

CLAIRE   Alan!

ALAN   What now. Oh, God!

CLAIRE   Look at this. Jamie lying in the middle of all this mess. Come on baby, hush now, it's all right, mummy's here.

ALAN   What's she been doing—records..books..your paintings...what's she been doing, Claire?

CLAIRE   Fetch her down, Alan. We'll deal with this together ....

(He goes upstairs.)

ALAN   Lisa! Lisa!

CLAIRE   She doesn't care. She just doesn't care about us. You and me. Jamie.

ALAN   Claire.

CLAIRE   What now?

ALAN   Lisa's not there.

CLAIRE   She's gone out. She's left Jamie like this and just gone out?

ALAN   She's gone.

CLAIRE   Gone? Where to?

ALAN   She's left a pile of letters...look at them..all addressed to me...Dear Dad...I won't be sending this letter... Dear Dad. Look at them. And this one. You open it. It's to both of us.

(Bring in train.)

LISA   Dear Dad and Claire.

I made a mistake.

I didn't want to hurt any one.

I'm going home.

Love, Lisa.

(Bring up train and fade.)

24

ROGER BURFORD-MASON
Keep On Running

My play is about the problems you can face when what you want out of life conflicts with what others want for you, or want you to do.

Jackie Wells is good at running and not much else. While her friends do well at the traditional school subjects, she only comes into her own when she is running. Jackie would like to develop this talent and become a first class athlete, but her ambitions require dedication and long hours of training which causes inconvenience to her family and Kevin, her boyfriend, who would like her to be 'normal' like other girls of her age. Jackie knows that becoming a great athlete is probably the only way she can prevent her life from being the humdrum existence which is so often the fate of boys and girls who don't shine academically, but she is torn by the conflicting demands of her running and her family and friends.

What should Jackie do? I have not given the play a conventional ending because in a sense we are all a little like Jackie, caught between what we would like to do in life, and what we feel are our responsibilities to others. For this reason, what you think she ought to do at the end of the play is as important as what I might have made her do. What advice would you give Jackie? I hope that in discussing it with your teacher and friends, 'Keep On Running' will give you the chance to think about the things you think are important, and help you to get clear in your own mind the balance between ambition and responsibility.

A final word to the lads, 'Keep On Running' has a girl for its main character because the problems we all face in making decisions about our future are complicated for girls by all sorts of traditional considerations about what women should or shouldn't do. I hope you'll discuss this aspect of the play too, but in the end make no mistake, these problems have no gender. Jackie's dilemma is common to us all.

ROGER BURFORD-MASON

CHARACTERS

JACKIE
MARY
GLYNNIS
MR WELLS   *Jackie's father*
MRS WELLS   *Jackie's mother*
KEVIN   *Jackie's boyfriend*
MISS BELL   *one of Jackie's teachers*
HEADMASTER
Extra Voices 1–6
Voices for WOMAN
          AMY JOHNSON
          SPORTS' COMMENTATOR

(*A cross country race is drawing to a close. Excited voices shout encouragement.*)

VOICE 1 Come on Jackie, you're nearly there.

VOICE 2 Head up Jackie. Don't let up yet. Keep going.

VOICE 3 You're miles ahead, there's no one near you.

VOICE 4 Go for the record Jackie. You can do it.
(*The voices reach a crescendo of excitement as Jackie wins.*)

OFFICIAL ...and number 107, Jackie Wells from Hancock High School, first in a new County Sports record time of seventeen minutes and twenty-eight seconds.

VOICE 5 Great Jackie, you got the record.

VOICE 6 Good old Jackie.

CHORUS OF VOICES Easy! Easy! Easy!

(*In assembly the next morning.*)

HEADMASTER My last notice will not be news to a lot of you because you already know that Jackie Wells of Form 5B won the County Cross Country Championship in a new record time last night. I gather from the P.E. staff that it was an outstanding performance and one which we can all be proud of. Well done Jackie. Stand up will you.
(*Jackie stands and the Headmaster leads rousing applause.*)

HEADMASTER Well-deserved applause, Jackie. I don't know much about cross country running but I can guess how much effort went into winning and setting such a rattling new record time. What I *do* know is something that Jackie doesn't even know herself yet. Just before I came into assembly this morning I had a telephone call from the County athletics organiser and he told me that after her marvellous run last night, Jackie was the unanimous choice of the selectors to run for the County team in the National finals next week in Brighton. (*Jackie squeals with delighted surprise.*)

HEADMASTER Marvellous news, Jackie. Very well done.

(*In the form room later.*)

GLYNNIS Brighton, eh Jackie? Just right for a dirty weekend afterwards!

JACKIE You've got to be kidding, Glynn. I'll be absolutely knackered after the race. I often go straight to bed after a big race I'm that tired.

MARY What, even races at school, Jackie? You don't do you?

JACKIE I do. I might get up about six o'clock for the evening but I'm usually too tired to do anything except sit and watch the telly.

MARY I don't blame you really, Jack. If I get caught for games on Wednesday I'm usually spark out for the rest of the day. I don't know how you do it, really I don't.

JACKIE It's like everything, Mary, if you do it often enough you get used to it.

MARY And you really honestly get up every morning and run before you come to school? Glynn says you do about five miles a day.

GLYNNIS We're lazy, me and you, Mary. We don't do anything really physical do we? We get knackered just running for the bus. I know just doing something like *that* really hurts sometimes, so what it's like running for miles and miles I can't

28

imagine. Doesn't it hurt Jack, all the running and the training? Don't you ever think about giving it up?

JACKIE 'Course it hurts. It hurts nearly every time I race. Sometimes I feel so sick when I'm really running flat out I could lie down and puke. And sometimes my lungs feel as if they're burning and the blood in my head is pounding and I'm aching all over.

MARY Do you mind, Jackie! You needn't be so bloody disgusting! You know even the sound of blood makes me faint.

JACKIE (*ignoring her*) But then when it's all over and I've recovered I feel... brilliant. It's ace, especially winning.

GLYNNIS OK Jack, so you feel good afterwards even if you feel dreadful while you're racing. But what's it all for? You have to train for hours every day. You get sick. You're too knackered to go out. You never meet your mates after school except now and again. What for? It plays hell with your life and I can't begin to imagine how you can have any love-life!

JACKIE (*quietly*) It's all right for you to talk like that Glynn, you've got a lot going for you. It's all I'm good at, running. You, you're good at English and maths and French, and you know how the computer works and how to programme it so it makes sense. You could have done history, geography, biology...anything you wanted. Any of the important things. Me, I can't spell and I'm hopeless at maths. I can't do French and they didn't *want* me to do biology, even if I'd wanted to.

MARY (*loyally*) You're good at D.S. and cookery,

Jack.

JACKIE   Big deal, Mary! 'Please sir, I'd like a really interesting job and a big wage packet. I can make nice scones and Victoria sponges and I know how to set the table properly.'

MARY   Well I wish I could.

JACKIE   No you don't, Mary. Not really. Not instead of maths and English and biology and all those things. You know, everyone knows, it's better to be good at those things than cookery or the things I'm good at.

GLYNNIS   Well *I* never got called to stand up in Assembly while everyone went mad clapping and cheering. It was amazing, Jack!

JACKIE   Cooking and running, Glynn? That's really good isn't it? I *don't* think. You'll get eight 'O' levels and I'll get a few minutes clapping and cheering in a couple of Assemblies. I know which *I'd* rather have.

MARY   Truthfully though, Jack. That cheering and clapping? Wasn't that…you know …a thrill or something?

GLYNNIS   Your name'll go on a cup, Jack. It'll go up on the Honour Board. Me and Mary, we'll finish our exams and leave and nobody'll remember us after we've left.

JACKIE   I'm not complaining. I'd have liked to be better at the things that count, but I'm not. Then I think that there are some that are so thick they don't know up from down. They can't do anything at all, not *even* running, so I'm lucky really. I'm a good runner. There's *something* I can do better than most people, and that makes me feel good.

MARY But you spend so much time on it, Jack. You've got to relax *sometimes*. You missed the last Upper School disco didn't you?

JACKIE I had a race the next day, Mary. I told you.

MARY Yes I know, but are you coming next week?

GLYNNIS Dancing Jack, that must be good for you. That's exercise. That's all I go to games for, the dancing. All those film stars do it to keep fit. They make records and write books about it, so it must be good for you. Are you coming?

JACKIE I don't know. Kevin wants me to go with him…

MARY)
GLYNNIS) *(together in amazement)* Kevin!

GLYNNIS Kevin Holland?

MARY Oh my God, Jackie! Kevin Holland!

JACKIE He asked me after Assembly this morning.

MARY *(comically)* Kevin Holland! Glynn, hold me up, I feel faint!

GLYNNIS You weren't thinking of refusing were you, Jackie? I mean, Kevin Holland! If you can't go Jackie, pass him onto me will you? That's what friends are for.

MARY Kevin Holland asked you to the disco and you're worrying about doing well at school! You never said you even *knew* him that well, Jackie.

JACKIE I often walk to school with him. I've known him for years. Since we were at the juniors.

MARY *(in mock amazement)* Glynn, she's only known the hunkiest boy in the Sixth Form for years without telling us!

GLYNNIS   Tell you what Jackie, I'll swap you 'O' level English *and* maths for Kevin Holland.

MARY   Well you're a nice friend, Jack. We've been friends for... since the second years...and you never even *mentioned* that the heart-throb of the entire female population of Hancock High was a personal friend of yours from way back.

JACKIE   You never asked.

GLYNNIS   That's no excuse. *You* know that just about every girl in this school fancies him   and   you   never   let   on. (*pause*) Are you going to go?

JACKIE   No.

MARY   (*aghast*) You can't be serious!

JACKIE   I can't. I go to Brighton the next day for the Nationals. I can't stay out late at the disco, I'll be too tired to run.

MARY)   (*speaking together in horror*) Brighton!
GLYNNIS)   I don't believe it.

JACKIE   (*defensively*) It's not my fault! Don't go on about it.

GLYNNIS   Kevin Holland wants to go out with her and she's going to stand him up for a race in Brighton. Mary, I'm going to cry!

MARY   What a waste Glynn.

JACKIE   He'll get over it.

MARY   *He'll* get over it! What about me and Glynn? I don't think I'll ever get over it.

JACKIE   He won't mind too much. He's got over it before and this is the biggest race I've ever had. He'll understand.

MARY   (*shocked*) Got over it before Jack? You mean this isn't the first time he's asked you out?

GLYNNIS   I can't believe what I'm hearing! Happened before? Have you stood him up before Jack?

JACKIE (*defiantly*) Yes, it *has* happened before. And I *have* put him off before. What of it?

GLYNNIS (*incredulously*) How many times, for God's sake?

JACKIE Only once. The last race. The County finals. He wanted me to go to his brother's twenty-first but I couldn't, I was that tired, I had to phone and tell him.

MARY The girl is mad! He didn't mind you standing him up? I don't believe it.

JACKIE He didn't, really. He's nice like that.

GLYNNIS Come on Jackie, truth now. Old friends and all that. Are you really going out with Kevin Holland?

JACKIE Sort of...I don't know...sort of...we just...

GLYNNIS (*in mock disgust*) Jackie Wells!

(*At Jackie's house that afternoon after school...*)

JACKIE (*bursting in*) Mum, where are you?

MUM In the front room love.

JACKIE Guess what!

MUM (*coming into the kitchen*) They made you Headmistress.

JACKIE Be serious, mum. Go on, guess.

MUM That Kevin Holland proposed to you and you accepted. That's nice dear. Now our Bobby can have your room. When's it going to be? I shall need a new hat. Will you put down for a council house or will you buy something? Those new houses up Windmill Hill are nice. Central heating, garden, garage with up and over door...

JACKIE (*laughing*) Oh mum, you're hopeless. Be serious for a minute. Guess what

	happened today.
MUM	Something nice was it?
JACKIE	Brilliant.
MUM	Must be to do with running then. What is it?
JACKIE	They've chosen me to run for the County in the National Cross Country finals in Brighton.
MUM	That's lovely pet. Running for the County, eh. Well love, nobody deserves it more than you do, all that training you do. All those miles you run every week. If anybody deserves something like that you do.
JACKIE	I'm so nervous already I can hardly keep still.
MUM	Your dad'll be so proud, love. But you'll have to keep calm and get plenty of rest or you'll not be fit for it. Come on, let's celebrate. I'll make a cup of tea. (*She starts to make the tea, filling the kettle.*) When is it love? We shall all be there to watch.
JACKIE	Saturday mum.
MUM	Not next Saturday, Jackie?
JACKIE	Yes, next Saturday afternoon. Why?
MUM	Not next Saturday, Jack. We're going away next weekend!
JACKIE	(*stunned*) Going away? No one said anything to me about going away. Where to?
MUM	It was to be a surprise for you and Bobby. We've arranged to go to Norfolk to stay with Uncle Norman and Aunty Betty. Your dad fixed it up weeks ago.
JACKIE	(*wailing*) Well, I didn't know.
MUM	They've just got a new pony and trap, and some calves and lambs to fatten.
JACKIE	But it's the National finals mum. I can't

miss *them*. Can't you put it off till next week?

MUM   I don't know, love. I'll have to ask your dad. He said something about next weekend being definite on account of something to do with some building work at the farm that's due to start. Some alterations Norman and Betty are getting done. Improvements.

JACKIE   (*very upset*) Isn't it real! The best thing in my life happens and something spoils it!
It's not fair!

MUM   There now love, don't cry. We'll see what your dad says when he gets home. Here you are, drink your tea.
(*Later that evening.*)

DAD   So that's how it is, Jackie. Betty and Norman start their alterations next week so your Brighton weekend is the last one they'll have free till God knows when.

JACKIE   But it's the National finals dad. If it were some tinpot little race like most week-ends it wouldn't matter, but the National finals…

DAD   I know, Jack. I understand how you feel, but we've *got* to go and stay with them. He *is* my step-brother and remember, they haven't got any kids, so whenever something happens to them…

MUM   (*shocked*) Don't you be so morbid!

DAD   I'm not being morbid, Daphne, but you know as well as I do, they *are* knocking on a bit now and they haven't got any children of their own. I don't think comparative strangers should step in at the last minute. Not when they've got family.

JACKIE But I've *got* to go to Brighton, dad. I *must* go.

DAD (*flaring up*)   Got to go? *Must* go? Who says so? Let me tell you my girl, *I* make the decisions in this house, not one of your teacher friends. When they pay your bills then they can tell you what you've got to do.

JACKIE (*in despair*) None of the teachers said it dad. *I* said it because it's something I want to do. I've *got* to do it dad. It's the biggest thing that ever happened to me.

MUM Come on now you two, don't let's quarrel about it. I expect we can find somebody to put Jackie up for the weekend while we go to the farm.

DAD It's not anybody's place to put her up.

MUM 'Course it's not Frank, but it *would* solve the problem, wouldn't it? You feel we must go to Norfolk for the weekend and Jackie will die if she doesn't run in that race in Brighton. How else are we going to fix it up?

JACKIE (*tearful*) What, go to Brighton by myself? You mean you wouldn't come to watch?

DAD (*crossly*) Have some sense girl. How could we come to Brighton to watch you *and* go to Norfolk. They're at opposite ends of the country. I wash my hands of it. If you want to go to Brighton you'll have to go without us. Me, I think you're daft to pass up a weekend at your Aunty Betty's for a couple of hours running.

JACKIE (*angrily*) Well you would, wouldn't you. You've never even tried to understand it. It won't get me a job. It won't get me any 'O' levels. It won't count at an interview. I don't suppose it matters that it's one of the few things I am good at and that lots of people think I could have a really good future running. If it doesn't put anything in a wage packet, you don't want to know!

MUM (*sharply*) Jackie! Don't you speak to your father like that. He's not one of your common classmates.

JACKIE My classmates may be common but at least they care about me. More than he does! I'm going to bed. *Good night!*
(*She slams out of the room.*)

DAD (*shouting furiously*) Jackie! Jackie Wells, come back here!

MUM (*to pacify him*) Let her go Frank, she's upset.

DAD I'll give her upset!

MUM She's only young, Frank. It means so much to her. (*sighing*) Pity we couldn't go to see her. It's her biggest race ever. Who knows what it might lead to. She was so excited earlier.

DAD Don't you start, Daphne. There are some things that are more important than just enjoying yourself, so don't *you* start on me. I'm doing what I think is right for the family.

MUM I know you are, love. I'm sure you think it'll be best for us all in the long run to go to Norman and Betty's. It's just that it's a shame that her big day should be the one Saturday in the year we can't go and cheer her on. I remember I was in the school play one year. In the juniors. I was Maid Marian. It was the only time I was ever in the limelight the whole time I was at school. My mum and dad didn't come to watch, I forget why, but I *do* remember I cried all the week. I couldn't enjoy it properly.

DAD   Give over Daphne. It can't be helped. It's a clash of dates. We can't go back on Betty and Norman now. Jackie, she'll be all right. All them teachers there. That Miss Bell she's always on about. She'll see Jackie is OK. She won't even notice we aren't there.

MUM   (*dubiously*) Whatever you say, Frank.

DAD   She'll be OK, love, don't you worry. She'll be that busy.

MUM   (*pause, remembering*) It was a lovely green dress I had, and my hair rolled. I thought I was the bees' knees.

DAD   That's enough, Daphne. You've had your say.

MUM   Me? What did I say? I just said I had a lovely green dress...

DAD   (*exasperated*) I'm going down the pub. I'll ring Norman from there to see if there's any chance of...

MUM   You do that, love. Have a couple of pints and give him a ring. I'm sure he'll understand. Tell him I don't mind staying in a mess if we *can* come later.

DAD   I'll try Daph'. Don't say anything to Jackie in case nothing comes of it or else you'll start her off again and we'll never hear the end of it.

MUM   I shalln't say a word love. Off you go. See you later.

(*Outside the gym after school two days later. Jackie comes out in a tracksuit after training. Kevin is waiting for her.*)

KEVIN   I thought I'd catch you if I waited long enough. You're steaming.

JACKIE   I had a shower.

KEVIN   How did it go? Tired?

JACKIE   Dreadful. I think I've got a cold or something coming on. I ran like a donkey.

KEVIN   Not too bad to go to the disco on Friday night is it?

JACKIE   (*deflated*) I told you Kevin, I can't go. Not the night before the Nationals. I'd best stay in or else...you never know, do you?

KEVIN   (*persuasively*) Oh go on, Jackie. One night. It won't hurt. We needn't stay right to the end if you want to get home early.

JACKIE   I can't, Kevin. It'll be smoky and the music and the dancing will wind me up, I'll never get to sleep. Then I'll be too tired to run and it'll all have been wasted. Besides, Miss Bell is picking me up at six. It's a long drive to Brighton.

KEVIN   Miss Bell! Brighton! Come on Jack, just a couple of hours. We can be back by ten.

JACKIE   Don't push me, Kev. See it from my point of view. I know what's best for me.

KEVIN   Best for you. What about what's best for me? For us? Are we supposed to be going out together, or what?

JACKIE   (*shyly*) You know, Kev.

KEVIN   But always the running comes first Jack. Running, running and more bloody running...and then me. Last week it was my brother's twenty-first. 'Where's Jackie?' they all said at the party. 'Home in bed,' I said. You can imagine the remarks! And I'm standing there feeling a .right bloody wally.

JACKIE   I'm sorry, Kevin. I said I'm sorry.

KEVIN   Yeah, I know you did, but that didn't stop you saying no when it came to the disco, did it?

JACKIE   What do you want me to do Kevin, give up running?

KEVIN   No, 'course I don't.

JACKIE   Well what then?

KEVIN   *I* don't know! Christ Jackie, you know how it is...No, I don't want you to give it up. I think it's great you winning all these races and all that. It's just...

JACKIE   Just what Kev?

KEVIN   Well...all the training Jackie. All the evenings you're out running. Couldn't you pack some of that up? Otherwise I hardly ever see you in the week. And another thing, you're always in that tracksuit. I can't remember when I last saw your legs, never mind your...

JACKIE   (*quietly but upset*) What you really mean is...can't I win races and be someone for you to show off about, but not go training or be a bloody nuisance and disturb your social life. That's it, isn't it? Well Kevin Holland, you're OK aren't you, because if it's not me there's queues of other girls who are ready to take my place. So you'll just have to find someone else you can swank about but who isn't such an inconvenience, won't you?

KEVIN   It's not like that, Jackie.

JACKIE   If I give up running Kevin, then what? What've I got that's worth a damn?

KEVIN   Bloody hell, Jackie, I just want to go out at night with my girlfriend. Go down the pub and meet our mates, the lot of us together. Have a few laughs. What's wrong with that? Give us a chance.

JACKIE   (*confused*) I don't know, Kevin. I just don't bloody well know. Why can't you just accept things as they are?
(*She gets up and hurries away in tears.*)

KEVIN   Hang on Jackie, wait! Wait for me!

(*The P.E. office at lunchtime the next day. Jackie knocks at the door.*)

MISS BELL   Come in. Oh, hello Jackie, it's you is it? I was just going to send one of the little ones to find you. We need to sort out the details for Saturday.

JACKIE   That's what I came to see you about Miss.

MISS BELL   OK, you first.

JACKIE   About Saturday Miss...
(*Jackie bursts into tears.*)

MISS BELL   Good heavens, Jackie, what on earth's the matter?

JACKIE   (*between sobs*) It's...it's...I don't think I can go on Saturday.

MISS BELL   (*astonished*) You don't think you can go?

JACKIE   (*sobbing*) It's all too much, Miss. I can't handle any more of it. I've had enough. I don't want to go to Brighton.

MISS BELL   What on earth's brought this about Jackie? Tell me what's happened.

JACKIE   Everything Miss, everything's gone wrong.

MISS BELL   Come on Jackie, you'll have to do better than that. I can't understand what you're talking about. What's the problem?

JACKIE   Problems Miss, not problem.

MISS BELL   Alright, let's hear it. Tell me all of them, one at a time.

JACKIE   Well first, I told you didn't I, my dad wants to go to Norfolk to see my uncle and aunt and *that* can't be put off, so he says. Then there's Glynnis and Mary, they think…

MISS BELL I shouldn't worry too much about any thoughts those two young ladies have about physical exercise, Jackie. It wouldn't do either of them any harm to smoke less and do something a bit more energetic than turn the pages of pop music comics. What else?

JACKIE My boyfriend Kevin.

MISS BELL Kevin Holland?

JACKIE Don't you start too, Miss. Why does everybody think it's so amazing that I'm going out with Kevin Holland? I haven't got two heads you know!

MISS BELL What about Kevin, Jackie?

JACKIE He doesn't understand either, Miss. He wants me to win races and be somebody so he can show me off to his mates but he doesn't want to be troubled by my training and running. It interferes with his social life! It's no good Miss, it's all a mess. If I give it all up everybody'll be happy, won't they?

MISS BELL Except you Jackie.

JACKIE I don't even know about that any more, Miss. Perhaps I *would* be happier.

MISS BELL Don't talk nonsense, Jackie. You're a natural runner. You could be one of the best because you actually thrive on the training and the racing. You love it.

JACKIE But how can I go on, Miss, when everyone is telling me what a waste of time it is? Perhaps it isn't such a brilliant idea after all. Perhaps girls shouldn't…

MISS BELL Don't say it Jackie, you'll make me angry! Girls have got the same right as boys to go as far and to do as well, and they

42

can, and it doesn't matter what we're talking about – maths, art, technology or sport. You're a brilliant runner, Jackie. You eat it up. You love running and you love racing. Why *should* you give it up just to please a lot of other people? What would *they* give up for you?

JACKIE   But there's my mum and dad, Miss. I know they'll be right put out if I don't go to Norfolk with them for the weekend. And then there's Kevin, he's fed up with it too.

MISS BELL   Your parents *do* have a right to some say in this Jackie and that's something we'll have to try and sort out. I'm damned if I can see what business it is of Kevin Holland's. Doesn't he go weight-lifting? Did he ask you if you minded him doing that?

JACKIE   That's different Miss, that's only once a week. Running is every morning and every night, and training after school most days too.

MISS BELL   Well, whose life is it, yours or Kevin Holland's?

JACKIE   And anyway, I don't want to upset my mum and dad.

MISS BELL   Then go to Norfolk. Give up Brighton. Give up running. Give up the one thing you excel at Jackie, but don't expect it to make you any happier.

JACKIE   (*in tears again*) I don't want to, Miss. I just want everybody to get off my back!

MISS BELL   Well they won't while you keep dithering. You'll have to make a decision. You're a big girl now, Jackie. It's time you decided exactly what you want and what you're prepared to do to get it.

JACKIE   Oh Miss, how?

MISS BELL   How about me coming round to talk to them, Jackie? Would that help? I could try to explain how much it means to you to run at Brighton. I could tell them what a bright future I think you have in running. I'm sure they'd be proud if you became a household name like Sonya Lanniman or Sebastian Coe.

JACKIE   Would you come round, Miss? They'd listen to you I'm sure.

MISS BELL   But would they *really* let you go and not come to watch?

JACKIE   It's this weekend in Norfolk, Miss. It can't be put off.

MISS BELL   So what will you do?

JACKIE   I'll stay with mum's friend down the road when I get back from Brighton with you. I've done it before.

MISS BELL   (*dubiously*) Oh well...

JACKIE   They'll be in this evening, Miss. You could call round after you've done your evening class.

MISS BELL   OK Jackie, that's what I'll do. Come on now, dry your eyes. You'd best dash some cold water on them, you don't want to go round looking like an advertisement for an onion peeler do you! (*Jackie goes to the door.*)

MISS BELL   (*calling her back*) Jackie, you're a runner. A good runner. Be proud of that. Tell Glynnis and Mary. And Kevin, tell him too. It's something real, more real than romance stories or a night out at the pub. Don't let them get to you.

JACKIE   Yes Miss.

MISS BELL   And Jackie...

JACKIE   Yes Miss.

MISS BELL   Don't make it too strong. I can't sleep after strong tea.

(*Later that afternoon in the library.*)

KEVIN   (*entering noisily*) Hello Jackie, Glynnis said you'd be here.

JACKIE   Just checking something for my project. Did you know that snails have got millions of little teeth?

KEVIN   What, all of them? Is that what you were looking up?

JACKIE   No. I was looking up 'Sweden, population of', and I saw the snail thing by accident. It sounds much more interesting.

KEVIN   Great thing, education. What about Friday night then?

JACKIE   I told you Kevin, I can't. I need the sleep.

KEVIN   Oh go on Jackie, be human for a night. Come to the disco. Just a couple of hours. I'll see you get home early.

JACKIE   Please don't push me, Kevin. Try and see it my way. Don't keep on at me.

KEVIN   (*coldly*) OK Jackie, if that's what you want. Me, I want to go to the disco and I don't want to go alone. Give me a buzz if you change your mind, otherwise... I'll see you around I suppose. Enjoy the race. Bye.

JACKIE   (*quietly*) Bye Kevin, enjoy the disco.
(*Kevin goes out with a show of nonchalance.*)

(*At home that night. Miss Bell has just left.*)

JACKIE   A great future, that's what Miss Bell thinks.

DAD   So it seems, girl. But running Jackie, what's that? How much a week is that worth, love? Do yourself a favour, run if you must. Round the block of an evening. At school if you want to. But don't let it interfere with real life, love. Your *real* life is here, with your family, or out having a laugh with your friends. Boyfriends. Getting married. Having a home. That's real life. Don't cut yourself off from it all, love, because one day you'll be finished with running and then what'll you have, eh? Just a lot of training and races to look back on. No boyfriends. No dances and discos. No parties and nights out. Not even much family life.

JACKIE (*quietly*) Perhaps there's a *different* sort of real life. Maybe boys and pubs and discos and having a family isn't the only thing.

MUM Norman and Betty were so looking forward to seeing you Jackie. They haven't seen you since you were... what? I don't know. Quite a lot younger anyway. You were just a little girl.

JACKIE (*passionately*) I've got to go. I've got to do it. Just to see whether I can. Whether I *am* a real runner or just a silly school-girl who's wasting her time. (*pleading*) Please dad, can't we go to Norfolk after they've done the house up. It couldn't take *that* long. What difference will a few weeks make? They'll still be there. Please! Come to Brighton with me and watch the race!

DAD I can't change it, Jacqueline. I've told you that. Mum can do what she likes but I'm saying no more.

MUM (*hesitantly*) One of us ought to go, Frank. What'll they say at school?

DAD (*exploding*) School! What do I care what the bloody school thinks! They encourage all sorts of silliness in these girls and then complain when parents don't go along with it! This is *my* family and I'll run it how *I* want and not be bloody sneered at by a bunch of hare-brained teachers who should know better. I'm going down the pub and you Jackie, you get off to bed. And while you're at it, just you give some thought to what your bloody running has done to this family tonight! Good night, the pair of you. I don't know what time I'll be back. Don't wait up!

(*He slams out angrily leaving the room in silence.*)

(*Jackie is having a disturbed night's sleep, hovering between dreaming and waking.*)

WOMAN   Jackie! Jackie Wells!

JACKIE   Who's that? Who's there?

WOMAN   You've got to believe in something, Jackie. If you believe in something enough you'll do the right thing.

(*There is a pounding of hooves.*)

WOMAN   Epsom Race Course, 1913. Emily Davison threw herself in front of the King's horse and died.

JACKIE   She was a suffragette. Who are you?

WOMAN   I loved to fly. I was the first woman to fly to India. First to fly non-stop to America. First to fly to Australia.

JACKIE   Amy Johnson?

(*An aeroplane approaches.*)

AMY JOHNSON   I might have been a housewife. Washing, darning, cooking. But I wanted to fly. To be free. They tried to stop me, of course, but you can't stop an idea once it takes shape.

47

Jackie	Weren't you scared?
Amy Johnson	All the time, but whatever is worth doing costs something. (*The aeroplane flies into the distance.*)
Dad	Split the family, that's what you've done. Come between your mother and me.
Mum	One of us should go with her, Frank. It's her big day. (*The noise of a busy, lively pub saloon bar.*)
Kevin	I'm your boyfriend, Jackie. It's normal to go out nights and have a laugh sometimes.
Glynnis	Have a laugh! (*She screeches with laughter.*) Look at that bloody tracksuit will you!
Kevin	Me, or the running, Jackie. You've *got* to choose.
Mum	I wish you'd come to Norfolk, love, it'd make life a lot easier all round if you did.
Dad	Waste of time. I've said it all along. There's no future in running.
Miss Bell	Use your senses, Jackie. You're going to make it to the top. Don't give up now. (*A crowd of spectators is roaring.*)
Sports Commentator	...and I can just see the first runner coming into view now.
Kevin	Disco, Jackie?
Dad	It's your family, Jackie.
Mum	...a lovely green dress. How I cried!
Amy Johnson	Nothing changes Jackie, unless you make it change.
Commentator	(*amid louder cheering*) Yes it is! It's the golden girl of British running, Jackie Wells, storming to take the race and the title... (*Cheers, applause, voices.*)

JACKIE (*anguished*) What shall I do? What shall
I do?

*A*udition

The idea for the play came from a letter I read some years ago on the problem page of a women's magazine. The writer was a fifteen year-old girl who had been disturbed to find some contraceptive sheaths ('condoms' as we are obliged to call them now) in a drawer in her parents' bedroom. She was revolted by the things themselves but perhaps even more upset by the fact that they were evidence of her parents' continuing sexual relations. She didn't know why this disturbed her so much but the truth was that she could neither get the incident out of her mind nor bring herself to discuss it with her mother, with whom, she wrote, she had a close relationship. In what I thought was a sensitive and reassuring reply the 'agony aunt' declared that she didn't much like the look of sheaths either, but they were undoubtedly an efficient means of birth control and, in this case, proof that the girl's parents were not only being responsible about preventing unwanted children on their own account but were also helping in a small way to keep the world from becoming over-populated. She went on to deal gently with the girl's feelings about her parents' sexuality, and especially about the existence of a secret, intense, other life within the household that seemed to exclude the girl herself. She recommended patience, sure that as the girl's own capacity to form intense and passionate relationships developed, so would her understanding; she ended with the light-hearted reminder that, had the parents not had sex then she, their daughter, would never have existed.

I wondered at the time how typical that girl was of others in her age-group. Not very, I thought: fifteen-year-olds, along with everyone else, are bombarded with information about sexual behaviour of all groups, so must surely take their parents' habits in their stride. Also, these days many of them are children of marriages that break up for reasons connected with sexual attraction — which suggests that some kind of dialogue about such things is carried on between the generations. How-

ever, professional workers in the field, whether agony aunts or marriage counsellors or guidance teachers, often comment precisely on the lack of communication in this area and report that parental embarrassment is still an obstacle to frank discussion. Published surveys have told the same story: a large group of parents still wants 'to leave all that kind of thing to the school and television'.

I wanted to write about a girl who feels these tensions within her family. In the play, Rachel's mother can't talk about her pregnancy partly because of her guilt at not really wanting a baby but mainly because she has always found it difficult to talk about anything connected with sex. Rachel's own shyness has so far inhibited her from forming a straightforward boy and girl relationship; all her intensity has been directed instead into acting and an unacknowledged crush on her English teacher. His sarcasm and her failure to win the star part in the school play plunge her into a mire of self-pity from which the down-to-earth comments of her street-wise friend, Kim, finally shake her. When she 'comes to' and recognises that her predicament is nothing compared with her mother's, she takes a step towards maturity and is ready to be both sympathetic and helpful when a crisis occurs. She's no longer standing back from reality, no longer 'auditioning', but playing an effective part in life.

ALMA CULLEN

CHARACTERS

RACHEL HAMMOND   *fifteen years old*
KIM   *her friend*
MRS HAMMOND   *her mother*
MR HAMMOND   *her father*
STEVE   *her brother*
JULIA   *seventeen years old*
BARNEY GRANT   *a young English teacher*
GEOFF   *one of Rachel's classmates*
KEVIN   *Kim's new boyfriend*

This play was originally shown in the Thames Television series The English Programme as part of a unit called 'Identities'.

1 House

(*Morning. A view from the back garden of the well-kept, terraced house that belongs to the Hammond family. Rachel can be seen moving about inside the kitchen.*)

RACHEL (*reading*)'… dead sisters. And that is all. And mark this. Let either of you breathe a word or the edge of a word, about the other things and I will come to you in the black of some terrible night…'

2 Kitchen

(*Rachel is going through the motions of making toast. At the same time, she speaks aloud – with some feeling – a speech from 'The Crucible' by Arthur Miller, a copy of which her younger brother, Steve, is holding and checking.*)

RACHEL '…and I will bring a pointy reckoning that will shudder you. And you know I can do it!'
(*She pauses for breath.*)

STEVE OK. You got it all right.

RACHEL Just a minute – I haven't finished.

STEVE (*briskly closing the book and handing it back to her*) Sorry. Rachel, I want my breakfast.
(*He moves towards the table.*)

RACHEL How about the expression in my voice?

STEVE (*not interested*) Great.

RACHEL Was it passionate?

STEVE Oh, yeh.

RACHEL Terrific part – Abigail: not the longest, but the best. If I can just get it right this afternoon…

STEVE What's this afternoon?

RACHEL The audition.

STEVE Come again?

RACHEL	The audition! When they choose who gets the parts.
STEVE	Oh.

(*Rachel sits and continues mouthing her words.*
Steve sits at the table and begins to pour cereal into a bowl.)

STEVE	Seen Mum this morning? Is she OK?

(*Rachel ignores him.*)

STEVE	Rachel! Seen Mum this morning?
RACHEL	I *heard* you.
STEVE	What's wrong with answering, then?
RACHEL	(*relenting*) I suppose she's OK. It's only stomach trouble…
STEVE	Dad's worried, though, isn't he? Keeps losing his rag since she went to the doctor. Really went for me this morning, just for leaving the hot tap running.
RACHEL	(*heavily sarcastic, as she returns to her book*) You mean you had a wash?
STEVE	Ha ha!

3 Parents' bedroom

(*Mr Hammond, Rachel's father, is making the bed. His wife, looking distinctly unwell, sits in a chair watching him.*)

MR HAMMOND	(*indicating bed*) You should've got back in here for the day –
MRS HAMMOND	Now don't start, Peter. I'll pick up in a minute.
MR HAMMOND	(*after a pause*) I think young Steve's getting a bit concerned.
MRS HAMMOND	I know. And Rachel –
MR HAMMOND	(*sitting on bed*) Not her: too wrapped up in herself, just lately.
MRS HAMMOND	No. I can see with Rachel. She knows, but she doesn't want to know.
MR HAMMOND	(*broaching a delicate subject*) You should

	tell her straight.
M<small>RS</small> H<small>AMMOND</small>	I wonder how she'd take the idea of another baby.
M<small>R</small> H<small>AMMOND</small>	If we go through with it.
M<small>RS</small> H<small>AMMOND</small>	If we don't, it's better not to tell her, isn't it?
M<small>R</small> H<small>AMMOND</small>	(*shrugging*) You could put it to her, discuss it –
	(*Pause.*)
M<small>RS</small> H<small>AMMOND</small>	(*After an inward struggle, she stands.*) You'd better send her upstairs, then.
M<small>R</small> H<small>AMMOND</small>	This *would* have to happen.
	(*He goes quickly out of the room. Mrs Hammond sighs and gets shakily to her feet.*)

4 Hall

(*Mr Hammond comes downstairs and goes into kitchen.*)

5 Kitchen

(*Mr Hammond comes in and is immediately irritated by the sight of Rachel poring over her book. Steve is bringing a pot of tea to the table.*)

M<small>R</small> H<small>AMMOND</small>	Is that a fresh pot?
S<small>TEVE</small>	Yeh, just made.
M<small>R</small> H<small>AMMOND</small>	Good lad. (*He begins pouring out cups of tea.*)
S<small>TEVE</small>	How's Mum?
M<small>R</small> H<small>AMMOND</small>	All right. She's going to work, she says. (*handing cup*) Here, Rachel, take her a cup of tea.
R<small>ACHEL</small>	(*without looking up*) Steve'll take it.
S<small>TEVE</small>	(*sensing trouble – he stands up*) Yeh, I'll go –
M<small>R</small> H<small>AMMOND</small>	No, you won't. (*Steve sits.*) She'll go when I ask her.
R<small>ACHEL</small>	Why? (*indicating Steve*) He doesn't mind.
M<small>R</small> H<small>AMMOND</small>	No, but I mind. And another thing: I'm

	sick of seeing your nose stuck in that bloody book –
	(*He snatches the book away from her.*)
RACHEL	(*furious*) Dad! I'm *learning* that! It's the school play –
MR HAMMOND	I don't care if it's the Bible. Your mother's poorly. (*thrusting cup of tea at her*) Now take her a cup of tea.
	(*Still furious, Rachel picks up the cup of tea and goes out of the kitchen door.*)

6   Hall

(*In the hall, Rachel stops for a moment and looks up the stairs apprehensively.*)

7   Bedroom

	(*Mrs Hammond, dressed as far as her slip, is standing by the wardrobe when Rachel comes into the room with her tea. She turns to her with an attmept at a smile.*)
MRS HAMMOND	Oh! Thanks, love. Feeling a bit groggy again – silly me, eh?
	(*Rachel hands her mother the cup and makes as if to leave the room at once. Mrs Hammond reacts.*)
MRS HAMMOND	Rachel – given up saying hello, have you? Or good morning?
RACHEL	(*dully*) Good morning. (*She kisses mother.*)
MRS HAMMOND	That's better. What was all that shouting about, downstairs?
RACHEL	Just Dad going for me –
MRS HAMMOND	He's a bit on edge at the moment, you know.
	(*Rachel doesn't want to hear. She fidgets.*)
RACHEL	Do you want anything else?
	(*There's another tense pause....Mrs Hammond finally ducks the issue.*)

MRS HAMMOND	No thanks. (*Rachel turns again to the door.*) Wait a minute – (*Intending to try again. Mrs Hammond stands up, but immediately feels faint. She sits again, hastily, this time on the edge of the bed. Rachel is alarmed in spite of herself.*)
RACHEL	Mum! What's wrong?
MRS HAMMOND	(*wryly*) Don't panic. I'm all right –
RACHEL	(*awkward now*) Perhaps you shouldn't go to work.
MRS HAMMOND	Oh, I'm better at work. I forget all about feeling ill when I'm busy. Rachel, there's something I want to talk to you about.
RACHEL	(*changing the subject*) I said I'd meet Kim this morning, early. We're going over our audition pieces.
MRS HAMMOND	Oh, the play at school. What's it called?
RACHEL	'The Crucible'. They are handing out the parts today.
MRS HAMMOND	Rachel…
RACHEL	(*suddenly animated*) Oh, Mum, I really want to be Abigail. It's a wonderful part.
MRS HAMMOND	Give us another kiss, then, for luck. (*Rachel goes unwillingly towards her mother and offers her cheek to be kissed.*)
MRS HAMMOND	You'll be fine, I know you will.
RACHEL	Fine's no good! I've got to be fantastic!

8   Road outside house

(*Rachel and Steve come through the front door and down the path. Children troop past on their way to school. Steve joins a group of friends. Rachel, her nose in her book still, presses on alone.*)

9   Bedroom

(*Mrs Hammond is dressed now and stands*

> *looking out of the window after Rachel. Mr Hammond joins her.)*

MR HAMMOND   Did you tell her?

MRS HAMMOND   I couldn't.....Get embarassed about those things at the best of times, don't I?

10   Approach to school

> *(Rachel turns in at the school gates and moves purposefully towards an outbuilding.)*

11   School outbuildings

> *(Rachel rounds a corner and comes suddenly on her friend, Kim, locked in a fairly steamy embrace with a tall, good-looking boy. She veers off and begins walking briskly away. Kim sees her, however, and disentangles herself from the boy and runs after her. She catches up; Rachel's face is like thunder.)*

KIM   *(calling)* Rachel...

> *(Kim catches up Rachel.)*

KIM   Sorry...just...er filling in time till you came.

RACHEL   How long's *that* been going on?

KIM   Oh, only the weekend. Bumped into him, Saturday morning, at the library, choosing a book.

RACHEL   What did you do? Help him with the hard words?

KIM   What does that mean?

RACHEL   He's stupid.

KIM   *(hurt)* He isn't stupid – *(capitulating wryly)* – Oof, he's moronic! *(She laughs: Rachel can't help joining in.)* Great kisser, though. Ooh, that'll keep me going all through double geography. *(ecstatically)* Better than smoking.

RACHEL   Cheaper, anyway.

KIM   Yeh.

(A pause. They have slowed down to a saunter, and are moving towards the main body of the school.)

RACHEL   *(moody again, pulling Kim into a corner)* Now look! I thought we were going to practise for the audition.

KIM   Oh, no. I've been thinking. I don't go for acting, really, not like you. I thought I'd see if I could help with the lights or something.

RACHEL   But you said you'd learn a speech.

KIM   I know. I got distracted.

RACHEL   *(indicating the boy)* By him?

KIM   *(stung – waves to Kevin to go away)* Who, Kevin? No, as a matter of fact, by my dad. He paid his official visit, Friday night.

RACHEL   Did he cause a riot?

KIM   Yeh. Oh, I used to think things'd be better when he left, but they're not. Knackers your concentration, anything like that.

RACHEL   I've had my dad up to here.

KIM   Why? He's not splitting up with your mum, is he?

RACHEL   No. But she's not well. There's a bit of an atmosphere.

KIM   Well, what's wrong with her?

RACHEL   *(guardedly)* I don't know.

KIM   You worried?

RACHEL   No. *(She is, of course. Another pause. They stop.)*

KIM   Look, we can get in this corner, if you like, and I'll hear you say your words.

RACHEL   No, I've gone off it now.

KIM   Come on, give us the book –

(Kim takes Rachel's book. Rachel snatches it back.)

RACHEL   No, I'm not in the mood.

KIM   Oh, never mind. You'll be nice and fresh

this afternoon when you do it for gorgeous Barney. He'll say: 'My God, it's Jane Fonda!'

RACHEL Oh, stop it, Kim.

12 *School corridor*

RACHEL (*not listening*) He said I was good in that scene from 'The Tempest', didn't he?

KIM Yeh.

RACHEL Oh, I do want to play Abigail in this.

KIM Sexy part, isn't it.

JULIA (*appears from behind and pushes between them*) Excuse me.

RACHEL Julia Wells'll be after it, too.

KIM Oh yeh, but she always overdoes everything. (*turns to Rachel*) You'll just have to give Barney your big blue eyes all through English this morning.

(*Rachel turns away, irritated. Kim follows her, grinning. They disappear into the classroom.*)

13 *Classroom*

(*Later that morning. Camera on Rachel who is clearly preoccupied and taking no notice of the English lesson in progress, although she never takes her eyes off Barney Grant, the handsome young teacher who is conducting it. Her concentration on him isn't just 'big blue eyes', however; it's more troubled than that.*)

BARNEY Well, that's dealt with 'constrained'. Now, is everyone clear about the meaning of the word 'constrained' as used in the passage?

PUPILS Yes...

BARNEY Sure?

PUPILS   Yes...

BARNEY   Good....Now, what's the next one? Um... 'obscure'. As in 'The precise cause of his fall from grace is obscure, lost now in the mists of time.'
(Rachel is thinking about her mother and hears the family's voices in her head.)

STEVE   *(voice over)* Seen Mum this morning? Is she OK? Dad's worried...

RACHEL   *(voice over)* It's only stomach trouble...

MR HAMMOND   *(voice over)* Your mother's poorly...

MRS HAMMOND   *(voice over)* Feeling groggy again, silly me! Don't panic...

BARNEY   Anyone care to take this one? Come along. *(Barney catches sight of Rachel.)* How about Rachel? Since she, too, seems to be lost in the mists of time. *(The class groans, all eyes on Rachel – who 'comes to' abruptly.)* Though the cause of your day-dreaming is obscure, Rachel – *(The class, except for Kim, groans again: Rachel is mystified.)* we'll forgive you if you tell us the meaning of the word.

RACHEL   What word?

BARNEY   The word 'obscure' as used in the passage. You know, the passage: on page fifty-one in the pink book.
(He waves the pink book, performing now for the appreciation of the class.)
'The precise cause of his fall from grace is obscure, lost now in the mists of time.'
(Rachel, now painfully embarrassed, looks down at the page.)

RACHEL   I don't know.

BARNEY   *(imitating Rachel)* I don't know... *(wearily, appealing to the others)* Anyone? *(Some hands go up.)* Er, Geoff?

GEOFF   Inexplicable, Sir.

BARNEY   Near enough. It's 'inexplicable' because

it's hidden from us. The precise cause of his fall from grace is hidden. So, it cannot be explained. (*He can't resist.*) Like Rachel's behaviour this morning – (*The class responds again – Rachel suffers.*) – which might have been affected by a late night or a quarrel with a friend or...

KIM Give it a rest, Sir.

BARNEY (*continuing*)... as in her case, by stage-fright. The dreaded audition nerves, eh, Rachel? But, ultimately, its cause remains inexplicable, or obscure.
(*Too much for Rachel. She endures it for a moment, then, with a sudden, violent gesture, sweeps books and papers from her desk on to the floor.*)

GEOFF Now you've upset her, Sir.
(*Barney looks at the heap of books and papers, then back to Rachel, who remains seated, gazing fixedly at the desk in front of her, her eyes filling with tears. Barney recognises that he's gone too far and tries decently to retract.*)

BARNEY OK, Rachel, you've made your point. Look, I'm sorry. It *is* Monday morning for me too, you know. Now, let's have that lot (*indicating the heap on the floor*) back on the desk and let us move swiftly on to, (*consulting his book*) er, 'baleful'. As in: 'There is evidence of a certain baleful influence exerted by a man called Richard Townsend...'
(*Rachel goes to recover her books and papers. Kim leaves her own desk to help her. The two girls kneel for a moment on the floor side by side.*)

KIM (*peering anxiously at Rachel, who is now weeping openly*) Serve him right, Rachel. Don't let him upset you.

(*Rachel doesn't answer. She and Kim replace the things on her desk.*)

BARNEY Anyone care to take that one? 'Baleful'. Anyone…?

(*But neither he nor the class can ignore the sound of Rachel's weeping.*)

BARNEY Rachel, (*helplessly*) perhaps it would be…

(*He gestures. Rachel raises her head and looks at him. Then, on a fresh burst of tears, she goes running out through the door. He turns to Kim.*)

BARNEY (*to Kim*) Go on.

(*Kim leaves the room.*)

14 Corridor

(*Rachel runs along corridor and down steps. Kim comes to doorway of school.*)

KIM (*calling*) Rachel! Rachel!

15 School

(*Rachel goes running out from school buildings towards the gates. Kim comes to the entrance and sees her far ahead, too far for her to catch up.*)

16 Bus-stop near school

(*Rachel goes running out of the gates and along the road beyond. A bus heaves into sight. Impulsively, she puts out her hand and it stops. She climbs aboard and comes to sit on the nearside of the lower deck.*)

17 Bus

(*Rachel is not crying now, but the face she turns to the bus window is grim.*)

18 Town centre

> (*Rachel alights from the bus, then pushes through the crowds of lunchtime shoppers and disappears.*)

19 Woolworths

> (*Rachel pushes through swing doors and enters Woolworths.*)

20 Cafeteria

> (*Mrs Hammond is collecting her lunch in the cafeteria and has reached the checkout when she sees Rachel coming towards her. She looks at her in surprise.*)

MRS HAMMOND Rachel – what's wrong? (*She pays for her meal.*)

RACHEL I just thought I'd come and see you.

MRS HAMMOND Have you had your lunch?

RACHEL I don't want anything to eat.

MRS HAMMOND (*to woman behind her in the queue*) Bring us another cup of tea, Joyce, would you? (*The woman nods. Mrs Hammond ushers Rachel to a table.*) Now, let's find a table... Here, that one'll do. Now sit down. (*She transfers a couple of items from her tray and looks at them ruefully.*) I don't really want anything to eat myself...Well, what's all this about?

RACHEL Nothing.

> (*Joyce puts a cup of tea on the table as she passes.*)

MRS HAMMOND Thanks. (*She pushes it towards Rachel.*) Have you had trouble at school?

RACHEL No. (*pause, she struggles*) Mr Grant made a fool of me in English.

MRS HAMMOND Who, Barney? I thought you were keen

	on him. (*Rachel nods.*) What were you doing?
RACHEL	Nothing. He said I wasn't paying attention –
MRS HAMMOND	Well, you should pay attention, shouldn't you?
RACHEL	He'd no need to show me up like that, though. (*Her eyes fill with tears.*) It was awful.
MRS HAMMOND	Come on, now. (*But Rachel is crying again.*) Oh, I don't know, Rachel. When I ask what's wrong, you say 'nothing'. But look at this; it's not nothing.
	(*Another pause. Rachel controls her tears.*)
RACHEL	I've got to face him at the audition this afternoon.
MRS HAMMOND	Well, you'll do it. (*a little impatient*) We all have our worries, you know. (*Rachel doesn't respond.*) I mean, *I'm* worried at the moment. And your dad –
RACHEL	(*uneasily*) I know.
MRS HAMMOND	Has that been bothering you?
RACHEL	(*quickly*) No –
MRS HAMMOND	Do you want me to tell you about it?
RACHEL	No.
	(*She is about to go on when Mr Hammond suddenly appears, weaving his way through the tables and coming quickly to his wife's side.*)
MR HAMMOND	Hello, love –
MRS HAMMOND	Peter!
MR HAMMOND	I've only got a minute. I'm double parked. How're you feeling?
MRS HAMMOND	Oh, I'm all right. All this attention –
	(*She laughs. He catches sight of Rachel.*)
MR HAMMOND	Hello, Rachel. What are you doing out of school?
MRS HAMMOND	Same as you.
MR HAMMOND	Oh. (*He turns back to concentrate on Mrs*

	Hammond.) I've been ringing your office.
Mrs Hammond	When?
Mr Hammond	All morning. You've been engaged, non-stop.
Mrs Hammond	We've been really busy –
Mr Hammond	I don't know why you don't take all this week off.
Mrs Hammond	I've told you: I'm better at work. I forget all about it then –
Mr Hammond	You're entitled. When do you ever let them down?
Mrs Hammond	Stop worrying, Peter –
Mr Hammond	I do worry. You know I do.

(*During this exchange Rachel has put down her cup and has been watching her parents closely. She notes her father's tenderness and concern towards her mother and her mother's responses. They have a kind of intimacy from which she feels totally excluded. She gets to her feet.*)

Rachel	I've got to go.
Mrs Hammond	All right now? (*Rachel nods.*) Give 'em all you've got this afternoon.
Rachel	Yeh. I'll be late back because of the play.
Mrs Hammond	All right, I'll remember. Oh, and Rachel … (*gives her 50p out of her purse*) Get yourself something to eat somewhere.
Rachel	Bye.
Mr Hammond	Bye, Rachel.

(*Rachel moves swiftly away from the table. At the cafeteria exit, she turns and looks back at her parents. Father has moved into Rachel's seat. Her parents are absorbed in one another, her father's arm resting on the back of her mother's chair. She had been going to wave, but thinks better of it.*)

21 Woolworths

(*Rachel emerges from doors.*)

22 Street

(*Rachel crosses the road towards the outgoing bus-stop. While she waits, she wanders towards a nearby sweetshop and goes in.*)

23 Sweetshop

(*Inside the sweetshop, Rachel buys some sweets, and turns to go when her eye is caught by a display of lurid, near-pornographic magazine covers. Her gaze moves over them uneasily. She feels disturbed and angry. Rachel leaves shop.*)

24 Bus-stop near sweetshop

(*The bus is waiting at the bus stop. Rachel dashes in, boards bus. The bus pulls away.*)

25 School sportsfield

(*Dressed now in sports gear, Rachel emerges late from the school building and runs quickly on to the sportsfield where a few girls are beginning to knock a ball about with hockey sticks. Kim approaches, ready for hockey herself, grasping an extra stick for Rachel. Rachel finishes tying up the laces of her hockey boots.*)

KIM Oh, here. You don't want *her* (*indicating games teacher*) going for you as well – not after this morning.

RACHEL What happened?

KIM Oh, nothing. He just looked a bit sheepish, that's all. Where'd you go?

RACHEL Saw my mum.

KIM Oh, what did *she* say?

RACHEL Usual boring stuff – doesn't matter...
(*She doesn't want to be questioned.*)

KIM What? (*calling*) Oh, Rachel!
(*But Rachel has dashed off to join the others. Hockey game begins. Rachel captures the ball finally and dribbles it off upfield.*)

RACHEL (*voice over*) 'Now look you. All of you. We danced. And Tituba conjured Ruth Putnam's dead sisters. And that is all. And mark this. Let either of you breathe a word, or the edge of a word, about the other things, and I will come to you in the black of some terrible night...'

26 School hall

(*Rachel is auditioning for the play before Barney Grant and two other teachers. The room is crowded with young contenders. She is nervous, her voice shakes now and then, but she manages to give a fair account of the speech.*)

RACHEL '...And I will bring a pointy reckoning that will shudder you. And you know I can do it; I saw my dear parents' heads smashed on the pillow next to mine and I have seen some reddish work done at night, and I can make you wish that you had never seen the sun go down!'
(*She finishes, looks relieved and then immediately nervous again.*)

BARNEY Thank you, Rachel. And all you other Abigails. Now... er ... we'd like to to confer for a moment.
(*He and the other teachers go into a huddle. General conversation breaks out.*)

Rachel moves to join Kim at a window.)

KIM   You were great.

RACHEL I wasn't, I was terrible.

KIM   Oh, well, I thought you were great.

RACHEL I can do better than that, much better. Got too much on my mind today.

KIM   (*indicating Barney*) He was impressed, anyway. (*pleased*) Oh, hey, listen: Nick Harry says I *can* work with him on the lights. How's that?

        (*But Rachel isn't interested. Barney is asking for attention.*)

BARNEY Um – we'd like to hear Julia again.

RACHEL (*to Kim*) Impressed with *me*, was he?

KIM   Oh, they couldn't believe she was so bad the first time.

        (*Julia begins her speech in the background as Rachel and Kim turn again to the window.*)

BARNEY In your own time, Julia.

JULIA   'I know how you clutched my back behind your house, John, and sweated like a stallion whenever I come near...'

RACHEL No, she's good.

KIM   Oh, don't listen. They'll have *you* again next; it's the tie-break.

JULIA   (*continuing, out of earshot*) 'Or did I dream that? It's she put me out, you cannot pretend it were you. I saw your face when she put me out, and you loved me then and you do now! A wild thing may say wild things. But not so wild, I think. I have seen you since she put me out; I have seen you nights. I have a sense for heat, John, and yours has drawn me to my window, and I have seen you looking up, burning in your loneliness. Do you tell me you've never looked up at my window? I know you, John. I *know* you. I cannot sleep for dream-

in'; I cannot dream but I wake and walk about the house as though I'd find you comin' through some door. You, John Proctor, that took me from my sleep and put knowledge in my heart. And now you bid me tear the light out of my eyes? I will not, I cannot! You loved me, John Proctor, and whatever sin it is, you love me yet. John, pity me, pity me!'
(During this Kim looks out of the window and sees, with incredulity, her boyfriend of Scene 11 go past with his arm around a girl. The girl carries a violin case.)

KIM   Oh, my God.

RACHEL   Sshh! What?

KIM   Look at that!

RACHEL   What?

KIM   *That.* Him, with that girl.

RACHEL   *(following her gaze, still not interested)* Oh. Tough, Kim. Still, what do you expect? *(She steals a glance back at Julia.)*

KIM   Oh well, I don't expect that. He's met her from orchestra practice; didn't know I'd be here, did he?

RACHEL   You said he was a moron.
(She lowers her head and closes her eyes, trying to shut out everything but her longing for the part, as Kim continues to mutter indignantly. The camera stays with Rachel.)

KIM   Saturday, he pays for the coffee and it's: 'I've never talked to a girl like you before; you're really unusual, Kim, dead funny.' And last night we're up the park, aren't we, under the rhododendrons, dead uncomfortable, for *hours* and he's saying 'I really enjoyed that, Kim, honestly, it was wonderful'...

RACHEL   Sshh.
(Kim tails off. Julia finishes her speech.

There is a stunned pause. Then applause.)

BARNEY (*a bit dazed*) Yes, well, um, thank you. (*He turns to confer with the teachers. Kim, like almost everyone else in the room, looks at him expectantly. Rachel remains with her face to the window, eyes closed, fists clenched. The teachers make up their minds. Barney turns to the aspirants.*)

BARNEY Right. Well, we think, um, Julia *just* had the edge there. So: it's Abigail for you, Julia. Nice try, all you others. Lots of potential there. And there's still all the smaller parts for girls to be cast yet, so I expect we'll fit you all in – somehow. (*He turns briskly towards the rest of the group.*) Now, will all those reading for the part of Thomas Putnam give their names to Mr Corlett, please.

(*Rachel is devastated. Kim collects her schoolbag and coat and puts them into her hands. Behind them, boys jostle into line for their own auditions and Julia is congratulated by a group of friends. Barney detaches himself from the teachers' group as Rachel and Kim make for the door. He heads them off.*)

BARNEY Nice audition. You came very close. But we just thought that...Julia's a bit more ...mature.

RACHEL Do you mean she's older than me?

BARNEY No, no, I didn't mean that. It just seems to be her part. Oh, excuse me just a second. (*to Julia*) Julia, first rehearsal is 4.15, Room 12. (*to Rachel*) Thank you. Anyway, we thought we'd give you a chance to do a bit of character work, so we've put you down for Ann Putnam – OK?

RACHEL (*not looking at him*) OK.

BARNEY So, if you hang about, you'll see who you'll

get as a husband. (*He nods towards the line of boys.*)

RACHEL No. I've got to go. (*She rises.*)

BARNEY Have you? Well, look, I really am very sorry about Abigail, but there's always next year for you. And I've got just the part: St. Joan. How does that grab you? (*Rachel shrugs and goes past him through the door. Kim looks helplessly at Barney and then follows. He turns back into the room.*)

27 Track by canal

(*Rachel and Kim come into view, walking dejectedly.*)

RACHEL I'm not going to do that part, you know – Ann Putnam – it's an old woman's part – she's nearly forty.

KIM Oh, come on –

RACHEL He was paying me back for this morning.

KIM Course he wasn't. Though you did go a bit over the top, didn't you?

RACHEL Well, I'd just had enough – from him and everyone else.

KIM (*stopping dead*) Oh, look, what's up with you? Is it your mum? (*A long pause. Rachel wonders whether to confide in Kim. Finally, she decides –*)

RACHEL She's having a baby.

KIM Is she? Your mum? Did she tell you?

RACHEL As good as. I knew, anyway.

KIM Well, is she pleased?

RACHEL I don't know. I shouldn't think so.

KIM No, not with her new job, she wouldn't be. And she's getting on. Here, perhaps she'll have an abortion.

RACHEL I think she's making up her mind.

KIM Ooh! Well, it must be a worry for her. And your dad.

RACHEL He's been diabolical for days now.

KIM Well, I suppose he feels responsible, specially if she's ill with it. (*a faint leer*) Still,
at least it shows they're close, doesn't it.

RACHEL Oh, shut up!

KIM (*startled*) Why, what's wrong with that?
It's better than my mum and dad knocking
hell out of each other. (*calling, as Rachel
walks away*) Oh, Rachel.

28 *Towpath*

RACHEL They really put me off my stroke today.

KIM (*ironically*) Oh, too bad.

RACHEL I don't know why they had to get into a
mess like that.

KIM Oh, they made a mistake, that's all.

RACHEL Yeh, just wish they hadn't made it so obvious, that's all.

KIM (*a pause*) Well, yeh. I know what you
mean, well, in a way. Makes you feel a bit
funny, thinking of your mum and dad like
that. When my mum was expecting our
Kate, I wouldn't go out with her. (*gestur-
ing*) Well, not when she was out here. But
I was twelve then. You've got to grow up –

RACHEL I might have done a decent audition if it
wasn't for that.

KIM Oh, you know, Rachel, you really are a
pain in the bum sometimes. (*Gets up.*)

RACHEL Who, me? (*Gets up.*)

KIM Yes, you.

RACHEL Why?

KIM Do you ever take a look at anybody else?
I'm dead pleased about helping with the
lights for the play. But do I hear congratu-
lations? Or three cheers? No, not from
you. *And* what about me seeing Kevin with
that other girl? I'm choked about that. Oh,

he's not worth it, but I am. And what do
you say? Nothing. Look, your mum and
dad are probably worried sick and all you
can think of is they put you off your stroke.

RACHEL   Yeh, well, it was important to me.

(*She stalks off.*)

KIM   Oh, but Rachel! It's only school! It's only a
play!

(*Rachel walks on, still disgruntled.*)

29   Alley from bridge

(*At the corner of the road Rachel sees an
ambulance drawn up outside a house in
the terrace. It takes a moment for it to
register that it is her house. She comes to an
abrupt stop.*)

RACHEL   (*to herself*) Mum?

(*Then she begins to run.*)

30   Rachel's house

(*Mrs Hammond is being carried on a
stretcher by ambulancemen. Mr
Hammond is with them. Mrs Hammond
is put into the ambulance. Rachel rushes
up.*)

31   Ambulance

(*Mrs Hammond, looking white and ill, is
lying on a stretcher-bed.*)

RACHEL   Dad, what's happened?

MR HAMMOND   It's all right, Rachel.

RACHEL   Mum...

MRS HAMMOND   It's a baby –

RACHEL   I knew all the time –

MRS HAMMOND   I'm bleeding. The doctor's afraid I might
lose it.

RACHEL	Oh, *Mum* –
MRS HAMMOND	I don't even know if I *want* another baby.
MR HAMMOND	(*climbing in beside Rachel*) We've got to go, dear.
MRS HAMMOND	Now don't worry, they'll do what's best at the hospital –
MR HAMMOND	Now, come on, Rachel.
	(*She bends to give her mother a quick kiss and then goes to leave.*)
MRS HAMMOND	Rachel. (*Rachel looks back at her.*) Did you get the part in the play?
RACHEL	(*a tiny pause, then a huge effort*) Yes! Yes, I did. Ann Putnam.
MRS HAMMOND	Ann? Is that the part you wanted?
RACHEL	Not quite. But it's a great part: real character stuff! It's just right for me.
MRS HAMMOND	(*all smiles*) Good girl.
	(*Rachel gets down into road.*)
MR HAMMOND	Steve, Rachel, I'll be back soon.

32   Road

	(*As the ambulance man secures the doors, Rachel stands waiting. Then he returns to the cab and, after a moment, the ambulance pulls away into the road. Rachel turns to see Steve hovering, awkward and white-faced, at the front gate.*)
RACHEL	(*jokey*) What's wrong with you?
STEVE	I'm scared. What's happening?
RACHEL	(*taking charge and moving him towards the front door*) Come on, I'll tell you all about it. What are we having for tea?
STEVE	I don't know. Mum hadn't got started on tea. Is she going to be all right?
RACHEL	Yeh, course she is. (*They are at the front door now.*) I know, how about you doing us some scrambled eggs and I'll have a go

at a chocolate mousse.

STEVE (*brightening*) Oh, if you like –
(*He goes inside house.*)

RACHEL And then we'll get ready for Dad coming
back, won't we? And then (*pause*) then I'll
ring Kim.
(*She follows him inside and closes the
front door.*)

Replay For A Plumber

'Replay For A Plumber' is a play for radio. Being dramatic in sound only, has distinct advantages.

Firstly, the play can range in epic leaps from one location to another and the mind and imagination of the listener accept the change easily; our minds work in this way daily in daydreams.

Secondly, fantasy is particularly potent on radio. Unfettered by images of the real, the imagination decides for itself how to construct the meanings into 'inner images'. Classics like 'Under Milk Wood' by Dylan Thomas, 'Albert's Bridge' by Tom Stoppard and the plays of Harold Pinter are good models for the budding 'sound' playwright. Harold Pinter's ability to produce tension and ambiguity in the silences was a new and innovative technique.

'Reply For A Plumber' could only be presented on radio. The sounds of the explosion and the necessary orchestra of sounds likely to be produced within a wrecked house are only possible in radio drama. The circular nature of the plot is also only possible in sound [you would not want to blow up two houses a night on stage!].

The idea of the play arose from a short story I wrote in 1979 about a businessman who wanted to put the world and the Government into a better state by blowing up Parliament and all those in Whitehall who ran the country. I felt the story, or another version of it, would make a good play for radio. I added the circular plot idea and then used the flashback technique to provide a tentative explanation for the 'bang'.

GERARD MELIA

CHARACTERS

SHEILA   *daughter of the house*
BERT   *the plumber*
PETER   *Sheila's husband*
EDWARD   *Peter's brother*
JENNY   *Bert's wife*
DOCTOR

(As the play opens, the sounds of a summer afternoon in the countryside. Footsteps are heard along a gravel pathway. They stop.)

SHEILA   Now where did I put my key? *(She opens her handbag and rummages inside.)* Oh dear, now what did…? Oh yes! I gave it to mother. Now what am I going to do? Good heavens, the door isn't locked *(She pushes it open.)* Perhaps mother came back for something. She's very forgetful these days.
(She enters the house closing the door behind her.)
Wonder if she's in the kitchen?
(A large explosion takes place demolishing the house. Sheila is trapped in the wreckage. A scratching noise is heard.)

SHEILA   If I could just free my damn feet… It's no use. *(The sound of dripping water is heard.)* God, my back hurts, if only…*(The scratching sound is heard again.)* He must be waking up. *(louder)* Are you alright, are you awake? Don't be afraid—are you badly hurt?

MAN   Hallo, *(pause)* hallo? Somebody there…is that Mrs Brady?

SHEILA   No, no I'm Mrs Brady-Smith…Mrs Brady's daughter. Do you have a torch or something?

MAN   Torch? Torch? Well, er…upstairs in my bag…in this …in this…

SHEILA   Oh please…please don't faint again…

MAN   In my workbag…a small torch…perhaps I don't…

SHEILA   You must keep awake. What's your name?

MAN   In the workbag…*(The rubble moves and showers debris on them.)*

SHEILA   *(coughing)* Are you still there? *(pause)* Can you hear me? *(Water is heard trickling through the wreckage.)*

MAN   Bert…my name is Bert.

SHEILA   Are you in great pain?

BERT   I feel terrible…*(coughs)* I've got this weight on me chest. It's a beam or something. *(He coughs again.)* Got a drink have ye?

SHEILA   Don't be ridiculous…Have you got a box of matches? Surely a man like you carries a box of matches?

BERT If I had I'd have a hell of a job getting 'em out of me pocket…I'm pinned by me arms, missus… and missus…I don't smoke.

SHEILA That's rather inconvenient…under the circumstances…Try not to worry, I'm sure we'll be rescued soon. (*Water is heard dripping.*)

BERT Could you reach up and lift this thing off me chest?

SHEILA In this pitch darkness I've no idea where 'up' is. Just a moment. (*She moves rubble.*) Good God!

BERT What's the matter…

SHEILA I'm slanting…sort of diagonal…I've discovered the back of the settee…the one in the hall. Least, I think it's the one in the hall…It is…I can feel the tassels. I'm practically suspended upside-down.

BERT Your arms are free then.

SHEILA But my feet are firmly wedged.

BERT (*coughing*) Every time I cough it creases me.

SHEILA Where do you think you are exactly?

BERT Well, I started on the landing like, there was this explosion like, and I wakes up here trapped. If you're in the hall I must be just above you I reckon.

SHEILA Does it hurt when you breath?

BERT Just a bit…I can manage…It's when I cough I gets it. I'm not so bad when I'm still. I reckon this beam has got caught somehow at one end. The gap gets wider as I move me arm along to me right. There's some kind of armchair a few feet away. Perhaps it's resting on it.

SHEILA That'll be the old chair from outside mother's room. It's Chippendale…Mother will be absolutely livid… What she'll make of this I can't imagine…I mean the whole damn place must be in ruins…(*Slates begin to slide in the wreckage.*)

MAN If you had a match you'd be a fool to light it in this lot.

SHEILA Oh…why?

MAN Gas missus…The gas main will have gone for certain. Bound to have gone…*no* messing.

SHEILA Mother had all the gas removed. When Edward

got depressed she thought she'd better go electric. (*pause*) The Police won't be long now. They're very efficient. They don't miss much in Epping.

BERT   I wouldn't bank on it if I was you.
(*The debris begins to move, wooden support beams creak. Sheila screams.*)

SHEILA   Oh God...God get me out of this. (*She screams.*)
(*The movement stops. In the ensuing silence water is heard trickling through the wreckage.*)

BERT   Missus...missus...Mrs Smith...are you there?

SHEILA   Yes I'm here...just...

BERT   Are you hurt?

SHEILA   No...least I don't think I'm injured...I seem to have been pushed hard up against a cupboard... No, it's not a cupboard, it's the hallrobe. I'll squirm my way across. (*She does so.*) Now, if I remember correctly, there should be a torch in there somewhere. (*She tries to open the hallrobe door.*) God, it's jammed. If I could get my hand inside...there...now it should be on this side somewhere...Got it! Let's hope the batteries work...Yes, yes we can see...Good God...we're entombed...we're absolutely buried. (*She begins to weep quietly.*)

BERT   Missus...missus...can you shine your torch up here?

SHEILA   What?

BERT   So as I can see what's holding me down.

SHEILA   Oh...yes...there...how's that?

BERT   A bit to the right...hold it, a bit more... That'll do. Now let's see. Could be worse I suppose. It's the bannister across me chest.

SHEILA   It's oak...Spanish oak...Hand carved.

BERT   Can you see anything you could use as a lever? A bit of boarding would do. Eh, the flaming torch has gone out! (*Sheila does not respond.*) Eh missus, where are you? Missus, come on missus, switch it back on.

SHEILA   I can't...I can't...

BERT   Why not?

SHEILA   Half my skirt has been torn away...and my blouse is in shreds.

BERT   Look missus, it wouldn't matter to me if you was starkers...

SHEILA I feel so embarrassed.

BERT   The feeling is going out of my legs missus, so for Christ's sake switch the bloody light back on. (*She does so.*) Thanks. Right...well, you can see what's happened...It's very plain if you ask me.

SHEILA It's a shambles.

BERT   Not quite. You see we've been a bit lucky. Fact it's bloody miraculous...We was both in the area of the stairs when she went up. There wasn't much to come on us, so to speak...Got that piece of wood yet?

SHEILA Listen!

BERT   What?

SHEILA It's the fireman's hose surely?

BERT   (*listening for a moment*) No Missus, that's the rain.

SHEILA Oh! Don't be so stupid...of course it's the fire brigade. (*shouting*) Hallo, hallo there. Hallo... we're down here. (*She waits for a response.*) Hallo...hallo...

BERT   It must be raining quite a bit. In wreckage like this, bits of roofing can channel the rain-water into the rubble...Then it tends to find it's own level like...

SHEILA That's very comforting. You mean we could survive all this and then be drowned as we lie here?

BERT   No...no missus, nothing like that...leastways I don't think so...

SHEILA You don't sound very convincing...Do you have special knowledge of these matters? I mean, who are you? You're a total stranger to me.

BERT   I'm your plumber. Bert Addley...Addley Brothers, Plumbers and Decorators, Peckers Hill Road. In Loughton. We have a contract to service your central heating and plumbing.

SHEILA Well I've never seen you before.

BERT   Look missus, I've been here regularly for the last two years. Now will you please find me something to prise this bannister off me chest... After that I'll be only too pleased to tell you my life story.

SHEILA Oh...well...yes...I'm sorry Mr Addley. I'm being

quite thoughtless, I'll try to help you.

BERT   I'd just finished putting two new washers on the washbasin taps in the guest room…and I comes out onto the landing like and *whouph*… I wakes up here.

SHEILA   Here's something…It's sticking out…If I can grip it with two hands…look, I'll have to put the light out whilst I pull this thing.

BERT   OK missus…now be careful.

(She pulls the object and precipitates a minor fall of debris. They both cough painfully.)

Have you got it? What is it?

SHEILA   It's a…It's a large rifle…It's Edward's…It's his new rifle…Edward is my brother-in-law.

BERT   For God's sake missus, watch what you're doing with it. It might be loaded.

SHEILA   Quick…quick then. Tell me what to do.

BERT   Can you lift it up and place it on my chest? Slowly… take your time…right that's it. Fine… Well, it looks unloaded…Take it back and use the butt to lever the bannister up.

SHEILA   I'll try Mr Addley but I must warn you I'm not a practical sort of person…

BERT   Slide the butt in here…near me right shoulder.

SHEILA   It's so heavy…

BERT   You'll do it easy…Now don't you worry, just follow my instructions.

SHEILA   That's easier said than done.

BERT   A bit higher up…now to your right…no…no… your right. That's it, a bit more…come on…just a fraction.

SHEILA   The ends wobbling about…and the damn thing's so heavy.

BERT   You're nearly there…nearly…that's it…Well done missus…reckon you'd best have a rest.

SHEILA   I've got cramp in my shoulder doing that.

BERT   You'll be alright in a minute…Wonder what time it is? Got a watch have ye?

SHEILA   My wrist-watch has stopped…the glass is so shattered you can hardly see the dial. It looks like twenty past three.

BERT   Unusual that.

SHEILA   What?

BERT   Your watch...having a glass dial...They're normally
          perspex these days.

SHEILA   My husband brought it back from Switzerland. He
          went with a trade mission last year.

BERT   3.20...How long do you reckon I was out...you
          know, unconscious?

SHEILA   I was knocked out myself you know...I've really no
          notion, it could have been an hour or more.

BERT   So we could have been under here for a couple of
          hours?

SHEILA   I suppose so.

BERT   But we haven't heard a bloody thing...in two hours
          ...I mean that's ridiculous...Surely somebody must
          have heard the bang...

SHEILA   Father did select a remote and secluded spot. Mum-
          my preferred the country after India. He was going
          deaf...legacy of the War...Artillery at Cassino...

BERT   Surely to God somebody has missed us by now. My
          wife Emmy must be wondering where I am by now
          ...surely.

SHEILA   So he opted for the relative quiet of Epping Forest.
          Do you know, he'd sit for hours in the garden by the
          stables...

BERT   (*interrupting*) Look missus, shine your torch up here
          ...Thanks...now...grab the barrel of this rifle and
          lever it down.

SHEILA   I'm not too sure...

BERT   Just pull down on it...That's it...go on...a bit more...
          go on, that's it...a bit more...go on.

SHEILA   I can't...

BERT   Hold it...hold it there...Right, now one last heave
          and I'll be able to squeeze from underneath...Ready
          ...now...come on, heave...heave ...heave...Hold it,
          don't let it drop...I can just move...Steady...steady...
          I'm nearly out...Done it! Oh Hell's teeth, that's much
          better.

SHEILA   Should I let it go?

BERT   Be gentle...Let it go slowly...That's it...Good.

SHEILA   Are you hurt badly?

BERT   Give me a moment missus...Could you roll a bit to your left so as I can wedge meself by that cupboard? ...There, that's better...

SHEILA   Is it your legs?

BERT   Just give me a minute...then I can take a proper look with your lamp. You can put it out for a while...till I sort meself out. (*He coughs and makes himself comfortable.*) If my Emmy would appear with a pot of tea I'd be fully recovered inside an hour.

SHEILA   It's certainly rather quiet, don't you think?
(*They both listen. A rifle shot pings out. Rubble falls and Bert starts a bout of coughing.*)

BERT   (*when coughing has finished*) Yes...it is rather quiet.

SHEILA   Sorry...I was just tidying the rifle away...I didn't know it was loaded.

BERT   Listen...can you hear anything?

SHEILA   (*after a pause*) No...no...I can't hear a damn thing.

BERT   After a shot like that...well, if there was anybody around, they'd be here like a...

SHEILA   ...a shot...yes, yes I suppose you're right.

BERT   I mean to say, a whole bleeding house blows up and nobody comes along to have a look...If this was Tower Hamlets the place would be a mass of kids looking for souvenirs...

SHEILA   This is not Tower Hamlets...

BERT   No missus, I know...that's why we're still down here.

SHEILA   Our nearest neighbours are only a hundred yards up the road...but they go to Ireland a lot... perhaps...

BERT   But this explosion could have been heard miles away.

SHEILA   It is odd...I must admit.

BERT   Yeh...It's a bloody rum-do altogether...

SHEILA   Peter must have tried to ring by now...He can be very busy some nights...It's been two in the morning sometimes when he's finished.

BERT   That's a bit better...The feeling's coming back into me legs...Where does he work, your husband?

SHEILA   Silvertown – he has a factory down there – next to the

	river quite near Galley Reach. It's near the new yacht basin.

BERT   Oh aye...I've seen some boats there that cost three times the price of my house.

SHEILA   We have one there...

BERT   I'm not surprised...

SHEILA   The river water supplies the water for the mill.

BERT   Corn mill?

SHEILA   Good heavens no...Peter owns a small paper mill. You know...high quality papers...Half the production is hand-made...Sort of paper used in legal documents. He makes his money manufacturing the paper for foreign currency...They have a big job on at the moment for a South American state.

BERT   He must be working overtime again missus. I'll just see if I can sit up...There, that's not too bad... Could you shine the lamp in this direction? Thanks ...Well, I don't appear to be too damaged.

SHEILA   He supplies stationery to lots of Government Offices too, including the Houses of Parliament...

BERT   Can you see any blood?

SHEILA   There's a cut on your head somewhere...it's run down behind your ear...Keep still...Yes, I can see it...It's not much, you'll survive.

BERT   I'm not too young to die missus.

SHEILA   (*laughing*) Really? Peter will be along any moment... I'm sure of that...(*pause*)

BERT   Don't you worry missus. I'll sort this one out... don't you fret.

SHEILA   I'd welcome a bit of light relief...Come on now, Mr Capable...how are we to get out of this lot unassisted?

BERT   Well you've made one correct assumption.

SHEILA   What was that?

BERT   The only way we'll get out of here is by our own efforts. I doubt anybody could hear us shout under all this lot.

SHEILA   That's crashingly obvious...so what do I do to help?

BERT   Can you see my workbag at all? It's brown canvas

with leather handles.

SHEILA (*she shines torch*) No...I think that's expecting a lot... Oh...God...Look look (*she screams*).

BERT Are those real legs in them boots do you think?

SHEILA (*crying hysterically*) They're Edward's new boots ... They're Edwards...

BERT Steady on missus...steady on...He could be alive... Let's get him out.

(*They struggle to pull him out and in doing so disturb the debris once more. They pull him clear.*)

SHEILA He's dead isn't he?

BERT (*after a long pause*) I'm afraid so missus...Who is he?

SHEILA It's my brother-in-law. He's Peter's brother. He lives – lived – with us here. You know Bert, this whole thing is getting out of hand. The whole thing is completely out of hand...out of hand...out of hand...: (*she weeps*).

BERT Stop it missus...Now come on missus...The only thing to do...the only sensible thing to do is to settle down and work out our own salvation... Pull yourself together...

SHEILA Poor, poor Edward

BERT He's well passed any help we can give him, that's for sure...

SHEILA Perhaps he's the lucky one...We might wish our fates had been decided so decisively...before... we've sorted ourselves out (*cries quietly*).

BERT I'll just cover him over with his own jacket. Could you ...? No, silly of me to ask...I'll put it – oh dear, I've spilled all his things on the floor...

SHEILA Don't touch anything...please...

BERT It's nothing much...small pair of plyers...a pencil... some old envelopes...What's these bits of things?... Look like bits of solder...and there's a mini-cassette recorder thing.

SHEILA He was a radio and electronics engineer...He wasn't a tidy man...living in his own litter...is quite typical of him...(*she sobs again*)...I did bits of typing for him. He dictated it all on that cassette usually.

BERT One of these envelopes is addressed to you.

SHEILA Are you sure? Edward wasn't a letter writing man... least of all to me. We shared the same house...Let me see. Looks as though he'd kept it in his pocket for some time...It's all creased and soiled. Could you hold the lamp a moment please?

BERT Is that alright?

SHEILA Thank you...
(*The voice of Edward reads the letter.*)
'Sheila my dear,

Things will have deteriorated so badly by the time you read this confession that the fact I've written it down will merely emphasise my cowardice. I couldn't tell you before this. There was always the possibility that Peter would relent and abhort this preposterous scheme. But you know Peter.

To begin at the beginning, as they say. As you remember, I was never reconciled to the termination of my career in the Army. It seemed rather absurd that a diminished mobility in my left leg was deemed insufficient grounds to request my resignation as a Guided Weapons expert.

I'd no idea what Peter was up to. His suggestion that I could make a substantial contribution to the business seemed loaded with sentiment. I accepted the post of Research and Development Manager, fully intending to seek alternative employment when an opportunity arose. I knew nothing about paper manufacture but Peter assured me it was a relatively simple process, and anyway, he wanted the firm to diversify, possibly into electronics where my specialised knowledge would be invaluable. He called me into his office one day...'
(*Fade to Peter's office.*)

PETER Come in Edward, there's a good chap. Help yourself to a drink. Soda?

EDWARD Please...It doesn't appear to be around Peter.

PETER Must be, damn it...Ah...ah...now wait a minute. Yes now I remember Dinky had it last...Pop your head

	round into her office…She's not in. I've sent her out to the bank. Wanted a private chat… very confidential you understand?
EDWARD	Hush hush, top secret, touch of industrial espionage is it? Should I test the place for hidden microphones?
PETER	Could you?
EDWARD	You're joking?
PETER	Cheers.
EDWARD	Oh…cheers.
PETER	It could become a routine matter…eventually.
EDWARD	It's hard to think why. Papermaking is a pretty open business…
PETER	I'm not thinking about paper. Do you remember I promised you the opportunity to help the business to branch out into electronics?
EDWARD	I thought that was part of your tactics to get me here, Peter.
PETER	That doesn't sound very flattering Edward, old lad!
EDWARD	Sorry Peter, do forgive me. Despite my painless initiation into the pulp trade, I'm still half expecting a little chat like this to deposit me into the bin marked 'Surplus to Requirements'.
PETER	My God, you do sound depressed. Leg playing you up is it?
EDWARD	It hasn't been too good, I must admit…but I'm liable to fits of depression, particularly after spending a weekend with my former colleagues in Germany.
PETER	My news should perk you up a bit. Another drink?
EDWARD	Why not?…Thanks.
PETER	For years now, as you are well aware, the mainstay of our trade has been our Government contracts, particularly in stationery requirements. Our new printing machines, which with your expertise have been computerised, have become an unqualified success. Orders have poured in from Europe and America which quite frankly we are really stretched to fulfil. The Board have decided to take up their options on the derelict factory next door and to

	treble our present accommodation. We qualify for Government assistance and local planning permission was granted yesterday. Building should begin in the spring. This is our opportunity to diversify our operations…and I've got an idea which is tailored to your knowledge and skills.
EDWARD	What is it?
PETER	The Ministry for Defence and in fact several other Ministries have been looking for some form of self-destructing mechanisms for secret and confidential papers. Captured documents have always been a major source of information and a major embarrassment to some after the trouble is over. The idea the Ministry would like us to work on is a type of paper which can be destroyed by remote control. For example if the paper is watermarked with an incendiary chemical and triggered by a radio signal, whole files could be destroyed. Is it possible?
EDWARD	The radio side of it doesn't pose too much of a problem. American Local Radio have developed transmission to do the job…in fact pirate radio stations over here in South London already possess equipment sufficiently compact for a car boot yet capable of transmitting over five square miles. Terrorists have used the shorter distance radio to drastic effect too.
PETER	You'll try then.
EDWARD	Of course. It's the kind of work I'm specially qualified for. I'm not your plain straight manager man, perhaps you've noticed?
PETER	I know…I know you've been restless…but this is just the opportunity. I'll see to the chemistry myself. I've got a small team recruited already. How long will it take?
EDWARD	Weeks, months, who knows? We've got no problems on the radio equipment, it's the actual ignition of the chemicals that will give us the difficulties. It's a fire we want, not an explosion (*he laughs*).
PETER	(*laughing too*) The chemistry won't be much of a

EDWARD	problem either. Take a man and collect some of this transmitting equipment as soon as you can. My team will work their pants off on the incendiary device, OK?
EDWARD	OK Peter, sounds an exciting project.
PETER	Prepare a preliminary paper with drawings, if possible for this time next week. The Board will want to discuss the idea fully and cost it out before the Ministry people start their side of things. It'll take a good six months to get initial permission and our new plant should be ready a few months later, OK?
EDWARD	Seems reasonable. I'll start now. Thanks Peter...

(*Now Edward speaks through the letter again.*)

'As usual with all simple projects that look harmless and easy when discussed in a comfortable office, the conversion of the idea into a working reality proved difficult and expensive. When the Fire Authorities appreciated the dormant danger

of files of potential fire-bombs in all the offices along Whitehall, there was a hell of a bust up. The project was cancelled and we lost money, a lot of money. Peter was raving mad. He lobbied the Ministers and pulled every string he knew. His appearance on television did no good either ...or so I thought at the time. He called me into his office a month later. He looked quite cheery. As a result of his TV programme he'd sold the idea and received orders from several foreign Governments.'

(*The voice of Edward reading stops abruptly.*)

BERT	(*to Sheila*) Well go on...why have you stopped?
SHEILA	There's no more letter to read. It just stops abruptly as though he's been interrupted.
BERT	We don't need anymore. What we know already fits together.
SHEILA	It's preposterous...Peter never told me about this...
BERT	It's preposterous alright. Your husband has developed a highly effective terrorist weapon. He could wipe out...just a minute...just a minute...just a minute...have you worked out the implications...good

God.

SHEILA Before you start to blacken my husband, let me tell you this, my man. Peter wouldn't hurt a fly. He's just not that kind of a man.

BERT He's selling missus. He doesn't care who uses the equipment. He's making money. His little scheme will be the most successful weapon of assassination ...

SHEILA I won't listen to any more of your nonsense. Can't we just concentrate on getting out of here ...Then Peter will clear up the whole thing himself.

BERT I doubt it.

SHEILA Why do you say that?

BERT He won't be around here for a while I should imagine.

SHEILA I don't understand. As soon as he learns of our... my ...predicament he'll be here to get me out.

BERT You don't get it, do you? Your husband has blown up this house.

SHEILA What on earth are you talking about? Why would he blow up his own home?

BERT Because your brother-in-law was about to spill the beans, that's why.

SHEILA That's absolutely stupid.

BERT How do we know this is the only explosion? Suppose he's activated his explosives in those offices... He's probably created chaos out there. Every building containing his note paper will be a mass of flames or a pile of rubble...That's why nobody has come to investigate us...they're too bloody busy dealing with his other demolitions to be bothered with a house in the country. He could have blown up half of Whitehall...,

SHEILA You're getting hysterical. (*she laughs*) I mean the whole idea of Peter...

BERT Blowing you up...perhaps he didn't think you'd be here...just Edward. I suppose you've large amounts of your own stationery in the house.

SHEILA Naturally...we store it in the... (*She pauses.*)

BERT	Where? Where do you store it?
SHEILA	In the cupboard beneath the stairs.
BERT	Supposing he's blown up all the emergency services.
	(*The sound of a vehicle pulling up is heard in the distance. They hear the sound of running feet.*)
SHEILA	Someone's coming. Let's shout. Come on. Shout.
BERT	(*putting his hand over her mouth*) Shut up.
SHEILA	What in God's name are you up to?
BERT	How do we know it's not your husband just checking that Edward – or you – are dead? If we shout he might finish us all off.
SHEILA	I'm going to. (*Bert punches her.*)
BERT	Not my life missus...not my life. Not my bloody life ...it's mine...I'm not letting some jumped up little Peter piss me about...not me, not me missus (*starts shouting*), not me you don't mess about with...
	(*Fade to hospital ward.*)
	Not me matey. You're not going to do me...
	They got me out then.
JENNY	(*laughs*) What on earth are you talking about love?
DOCTOR	Just one moment Mrs Addley. I'd like to examine him.
JENNY	Oh. Right doctor, shall I leave?
DOCTOR	No. It won't take a minute. Now Mr Addley, just look towards me. I'll just shine a light in your eye. It won't hurt. That's it. (*pause*) Good. Now the other...(*pause*) Good. Well Addley, nothing to worry about. You're a very lucky man. A fall from that height can cause much more damage than you appear to have sustained. We'll keep an eye on you for a few days, then we'll see about letting you home.
BERT	Thank you doctor. Thanks... (*Doctor leaves.*)
JENNY	You've had us all worried.
BERT	Oh.
JENNY	You've been out for nearly twenty-four hours.
BERT	Well, I remember them coming to get us out and shouting but nothing after that.
JENNY	I think you're a bit confused love. Don't you remem-

ber what happened?

BERT Yes. I was doing these taps, and then this explosion.

JENNY (*laughing*) Doctor said you'd be a bit confused. No love. You fell off the ladder inspecting the central heating outlet at Mr Hudson's house out in Turbridge. It's affected your memory, that's obvious. Don't worry love. It'll all come back.

BERT Mr Hudson's? Mr Hudson's? No no, I did Delaney's Farm, then Mrs Brady-Smith's.

JENNY Oh dear. It has affected you. They're not due for servicing them folk till next month.

BERT Are you sure?

JENNY Mrs Brady-Smith wrote from London reminding us only yesterday. Poor woman.

BERT Poor woman. Why?

JENNY Well, I don't know why she keeps that big house on. She's seldom there.

BERT Her daughter looks after the place doesn't she?

JENNY Look love, just rest yourself. Don't talk too much. You'll just confuse yourself. You just have a snooze, and I'll see you in the morning. (*She kisses him.*) Goodnight love.

BERT Goodnight Jenny. Goodnight. Oh Jenny!

JENNY Yes love?

BERT Did they get her out too.

JENNY Who love?

BERT Mrs Brady's daughter.
(*Pause.*)

JENNY Er..yes love. I'm sure they did. Now go to sleep, there's a good lad. See you in the morning.

BERT Good, I'm glad they got her out – very glad, very glad indeed.
(*Fade. Sounds of bacon frying in the home of Bert Addley one month later.*)

JENNY Three rashers or four, Bert?

BERT Just three love.

JENNY Are you sure? Got to keep your strength up first day back at work.

BERT No. I don't feel hungry really.

JENNY   Bet you're glad to be back after all these weeks.

BERT   Yeh. Dead boring. Just sitting here watching the telly. Fancy four weeks of telly in the afternoon.

JENNY   Have you taken your tablets?

BERT   Yep.

JENNY   Don't want you relapsing into your little daydreams.

BERT   What do you mean?

JENNY   Well you know, about your secret woman.

BERT   Oh come on. It was just something I dreamt when I was unconscious like. Just like the doctor said.

JENNY   Yes but fancy picking on her. Sheila Brady-Smith wouldn't be too happy about being blown up with the likes of you, love.

BERT   It was just a dream.

JENNY   Now remember what the doctor said: go careful. He said you may get a dizzy spell or feel strange. Just sit down and rest. And don't take any notice of this dream you had.

BERT   This fellah in the wreckage wore paratroops' boots and this rifle.

JENNY   It's all a dream. Forget it.

BERT   What's today's calls?

JENNY   Well, there's Rutherfords down by the quarry. Company offices have asked to have their washbasins replaced, but that can wait. (*The phone rings.*)

JENNY   (*picking up the phone*) Hallo. O hallo Mr Delaney (*pause*). He's right here. Hold on. It's for you – he's had a big burst.

BERT   Hallo Mr Delaney. Yes...yes...I see. No water at all. I see...right...right. Well I'll call on you first. OK, fine. Cheerio Mr Delaney. (*putting down the phone*) He's had a blockage somewhere. He can't get water to the animals. I'll start there.

JENNY   It's the Brady-Smiths' turn for servicing. It's quite a big job. Didsbury Hall usually takes a whole afternoon, as you well know.

BERT   I'll call there after Delaney's (*pause*).

JENNY   What's the matter? You're not ill are you?

BERT   No, no. Just a silly notion I had, you know the feel-

	ing. As though you'd done it before.
JENNY	Oh God, Bert. We've all had that. Right. I'll go down to the office. You can phone me there if you want anything.
BERT	Right. OK (*kisses her*).
JENNY	Take it easy, Bert. You'll be alright.
BERT	Sure, sure.
	(*Fade to sound of Bert driving his car and whistling.*)
BERT	Aye aye, somebody thumbing a lift. Been out shooting by the looks of things. (*He pulls up by the side of the hitch-hiker.*)
MAN	Can you possibly give me a lift? My car's broken. Half-shafts gone, I'm afraid. I'll phone the garage from Didsbury Hall.
BERT	That's where I'm going. Jump in.
MAN	That's a slice of luck. Thanks old chap. Can you find room for this? It's just a sample. (*The car starts and moves off.*) It's not loaded. I've just collected it from town, I'm going to Africa, a safari of sorts. My first time.
BERT	Elephant gun it looks like.
MAN	Something like that.
BERT	Thought the hall was empty in the winter.
MAN	Well, it is usually but my sister-in-law – Mrs Brady, that is – has a soft spot for me. She's arriving tonight. Kind of farewell-do, so to speak. I'm Edward Carrington.
BERT	Bert Addley.
EDWARD	Pleased to meet you.
BERT	I'm on my way to service the plumbing.
EDWARD	About time too. Place sounds haunted at night. There's so much air trapped in the pipes.
BERT	(*laughing*) Well we'll have to see about that, won't we?
	(*Fade to both men unlocking the front door.*)
BERT	After you Sir.
EDWARD	Right. Now where shall I put this damn thing?
BERT	Straight upstairs is it, for Mrs Brady's bedroom?
EDWARD	That's right. Along the landing and it's the door facing you. I can't come and show you wearing these boots.

They're part of my safari equipment. Ex-Army and Navy, but they'll do I suppose, when I've broken them in. See you later (*exits into kitchen*).

BERT   Oh God. My mind – my mind's going again. I must be deluded or whatever they call it. I've seen all this before. I can't go on. I just can't (*pause*). (*Voice of wife*) 'We don't want you relapsing into your little day-dreams, do we? Have you taken your tablet? Day dreams about your secret woman, eh! (*she laughs*) Secret woman me! Have you taken your tablet?... tablet... tablet!...'
Must pull myself together. People might think I'm barmy. It's just the effects of that fall. Now where's the shoes. Ah, there they are (*puts them on*). Now in we go.
(*Fade to sounds of a summer afternoon in the countryside. Footsteps are heard walking along the gravel pathway. They stop. Thunder is heard in the distance.*)

SHEILA   Now where did I put my key? (*She opens her handbag and rummages inside.*) Oh dear, now what did...?Oh yes! I gave it to mother. Now what am I going to do? Good heavens, the door isn't locked. (*She pushes it open.*) Perhaps mother came back for something, she's so forgetful these days.
(*She enters the house closing the door behind her.*)
Wonder if she's in the kitchen?

A large explosion takes place demolishing the house.

JOHN TURNER
AND IAN MCMILLAN

*M*etamorphosid Arkwright

In the short story 'Metamorphosis' by Franz Kafka, the unfortunate Gregor turns into a beetle overnight and suffers ridicule and rejection at the hands of his family and friends. In 'Metamorphosid Arkwright', we wanted to examine the transformation process at closer quarters. We therefore made Sid, the central character, turn into a cockroach gradually, over the period of a couple of weeks. This allowed us to observe the development of the reactions of those close to him, from initial sympathy and understanding through to ultimate rejection and hostility.

The play is intended foremost to be a black comedy, but also a moral fable set in the closed world of Northern Working Men's Clubs. These clubs are often bastions of traditional values, operated to rigid rules, administered by a male oligarchy. (In fact, one of the authors has been disciplined by a club for talking too excitedly during a bingo session.)

The play was written especially for radio; the concept of a character slowly changing into a cockroach while retaining, for the most part, human powers of speech, is one ideally suited for this medium.

You'll notice that the scenes get shorter as the play progresses to reflect the gathering pace of Sid's transformation, then slows down in the last scene where....but you must find out for yourself.

Enjoy the play, laugh at the jokes. It is our belief as writers that if you have a message to get across to your audience, the most effective way to do so is to entertain and amuse them.

JOHN TURNER
IAN McMILLAN

CHARACTERS

SID
ALBERT
HARRY
ERIC   Sid's son
DORA   Sid's wife
FRED
EL MAGICO
MAUREEN
ADA

This play was first broadcast on Radio 4 from New Broadcasting House, Manchester, on Friday, 6th May 1983 (directed by Alfred Bradley).

Performance Note   *The words* Rattle Rattle *have been used in the text to describe the 'cockroach' noise made by Sid during his metamorphosis. The authors envisage this resembling a sort of guttural, gargling sound.*

(*Fade in.*)

ALBERT   Right then, gentlemen, it being twelve noon, I declare this Committee Meeting open. Now, any apologies for absence?

HARRY   All present and correct, Albert, er Mr Chairman, I mean — except old Sid. Funny that, never known him miss a meeting before.

ALBERT   Aye it's rum, it is, you can set your watch by Sid — always gets here bang on five to — but as it's the time appointed and as we've got a quorum, I suppose we'll have to make a start, Sid or no Sid.

FRED   Hang on a second, Albert, Sid's never missed a Committee Meeting in his life. It'd take an earthquake to keep him away. Just give him a minute.

ALBERT   I know all about that Fred, Sid's my oldest mate, but club rules is club rules and we've got a lot to get through on agenda. Now then, item one…
(*Door opens.*)

ALBERT   Sid! You had us worried there a minute.

SID   Sorry I'm late, lads, car wouldn't start. Bloody flat battery.

ALBERT   Aye, it's 'cold weather, had a bit o' trouble with mine this morning. Anyway, sit down Sid, we've just started. Hey up! What's up with your arm?

SID   Ey, I don't know. Rheumatic attack, I think.

ALBERT   Doctor told you to put it in that sling then?

SID   Aye, said I'd have to keep it on for, well, for a few weeks I think. Might even be months.

ALBERT   Ee, I'm right sorry to hear that, Sid, lad. It's not your darts arm is it?

SID   No, it's t'other 'un. I'll be alright for 'matches.

FRED   Thank goodness for that – it's the big 'un this week – promotion might rest on't outcome – can't afford to lose 'darts captain with 'divisional championship at stake.

ALBERT   (*clears throat*) Well, let's get back to business, eh lads? Right, gentlemen, meeting of the Westthorpe Social Club Committee. Item one: Minutes of last meeting — I think we'll take them as read. Any matters arising?

HARRY Aye, I want to raise something. This rubbish about making Mondays ladies' night — you're going to have to watch 'em Albert. I caught two of 'em on 'snooker table last Monday. Got a right mouthful from 'em, I don't mind telling you, before I got 'em off 'table. You can't have lady members playing snooker. The club'd become a laughing stock. Anyway, women are the wrong shape for it, when they get down for their shot, they er, spread their frontespieces all over 'table top, if you see what I mean. Wears out the nap.

ALBERT Point taken, Harry, lad. We'll lock off 'games room Monday nights in future. (*pause*) Anything else?

SID Aye, about my son's reception, Albert. Any chance of getting 'bingo machine moved for t'afternoon. Last wedding reception I went to in 'club, all 'guests were queuing up for 'three-bob flyer in 'middle of 'groom's speech.

ALBERT Aye, I think we can er.... Hey, you alright Sid, lad? You look to be in pain.

SID It's my arm, that's all. Bloody sling's too tight.

FRED Here, let me have a look — I've done a bit of St John's — now then aye, it is a bit tight!

SID Gerrof Fred you gormless idiot! It's alright I tell you, mind your own bloody business.

ALBERT Sid! I'm surprised at you lad. I've never known you go off like that. The Committee room is no place for such behaviour.

FRED I were only trying to help.

SID Forget it, let's just gerron with 'meeting shall we?

ALBERT Aye, I reckon we better had. Harry, what are you doing?

HARRY I'm just looking at 'filling in this here sandwich missus has packed me up. Ugh, I don't know what it is, but it looks like a squashed beetle, ugh, smells like it an' all.

SID (*angry*) What did you say, Harry Micklethwaite!

HARRY   Eh?

SID   You said your sandwich looked like a squashed beetle. I think that's in very bad taste. Take it back at once.

HARRY   You what?

SID   You take it back or I'll knock you down them stairs.

HARRY   Now look here Sid Arkwright.

ALBERT   Sid, Harry, knock it off, pair on you. Ee, I don't know, Sid, I think you got out of wrong side of 'bed this morning. Why don't you go downstairs and get yourself a pint and calm down, eh? I'll see you after 'meeting.

SID   (*quietly*) Aye, I think I might. Sorry Albert, don't know what came over me. See you.

ALBERT   Right then, if we can try and get through this meeting before closing time....
(*Fade out.*)
(*Fade in. Door opening and closing.*)

ERIC   Hello Dad — is that you?

SID   Aye.

ERIC   Meeting's over early.

SID   Noah — left before it finished — me arm's playing up.

ERIC   You want to get to 'doctors with that arm. I don't understand what all 'secrecy is about anyway. You won't let anyone have a look at it....

SID   I wish folk'd shut up about my arm — first bloody committee men and now you — just give it a rest!

ERIC   Well, if that's the way you feel about it....

SID   Oh, we discussed that bingo machine, it'll be shifted for 'reception. Has your mam ordered the flowers yet?

ERIC   I think so, hey Dad —

SID   Yes, Eric.

ERIC   Do we have to hold 'reception in that out-of-date old club?

SID   Out-of-date? It were completely redecorated and refurnished in't spring — won 'club of the year

101

award. Cheeky young....

ERIC No. I mean out-of-date folk. Dad, look I'm in a different mould to them as goes down there every night. I'm a rising young businessman.

SID Businessman? You mend television sets!

ERIC Aye, I know, but it's my own set up — got my own van and soon I'll be opening up a shop if I get my bank loan.

SID Aye, and pigs might fly.

ERIC Listen Dad. I know 'real reason why you want me to have 'do in concert room at 'club, you're scared to offend that precious committee of yours.

SID No, Eric, it's not that. You know I want the best for you and for your Sharon, I want you to do well. But it's a tradition lad, something you young 'uns wouldn't understand. All 'committee men have had their sons' and daughters' receptions in 'club. I've been part of that club for years, I remember it when it were just a building site and me and Albert and a couple of others were standing there in 'mud with t'architect's plans in our hands. Sometimes I think — and I don't want you to take this 'wrong way, Eric, lad — that 'club and what it stands for is as important to me as my family is, and don't forget that's where you and Sharon met — at a junior dance there, years ago.

ERIC I know all that, Dad, but I'm not like you. I'm trying to get out o' club scene — down there every night, supping and playing darts and dominoes. I want to escape from all that. I've got ambitions, I want to better myself. Anyway, people's tastes are getting more sophisticated, Dad. I reckon the days of the working men's clubs are numbered.

SID Never! There'll always be clubs.

ERIC Well, I've said my piece.

SID Aye, you have.

ERIC But I suppose Sharon's Dad — seeing as he's a committee man an' all — will have been working on her. So I'll go along with it — for your sake, Dad — 'cos I know how much it means to you, but after 'reception you'll not catch me setting foot in that club again, alright?

SID   Fair enough. You're a good son, Eric, I knew you wouldn't let me down. It won't be so bad you know. 'Club Steward puts on a right good spread …. (*pause*) Hey, you gonna mash then? I fancy a cup of tea.

(*Fade out.*)

(*Fade in bedroom.*)

DORA   Are you coming up to bed, Sid?

SID   (*muffled reply*)

DORA   Hurry up, it's late. I want to get some sleep.

SID   Sorry Dora.

DORA   Bloody hell, what are you up to, Sid Arkwright? Taking the dog for a walk or summat? Come on, get into bed and take that silly coat off.

SID   I'm cold, that's all, bloody perishing in here.

DORA   Don't be barmy, it's red hot, I've had central heating on. Are you coming down with summat?

SID   I'm just feeling the cold a bit today, love, that's all. I'm not a spring chicken anymore you know.

DORA   Hey, you're not getting into bed wearing that thing are you?

SID   Lots of people wear coats in bed.

DORA   Do they hellers like. Hey, aren't you even going to unfasten it?

SID   Just turn 'light off love and go to sleep.

DORA   Is it your arm that's making you act so funny love? Let's have a look. Here, take that daft coat off and show me….

SID   No, ow! (*sharp intake of breath*) That hurt.

DORA   I think you ought to see 'doctor with that.

SID   It's just a slight swelling, that's all. (*Rattle Rattle, cough*) Something in me throat. Aye, I'll be as right as ninepence in 'morning. (*Rattle Rattle*)

DORA   What's that? What's that noise? Is that you?

SID   Er, what? No. Pipes rattling I think. Bloody

103

plumbers — never do 'job right.

DORA   Come to bed Sid. You can keep your coat on if you must. But tomorrow you're off to 'doctors. I reckon he needs to take a look at you. I think that bad arm's making you go soft in 'head. Ouch, mind that buckle.

SID   Sorry love.

DORA   Goodnight then.

SID   Goodnight Dora. (*Rattle Rattle*)
(*Fade out.*)
(*Fade in bar noise.*)

ALBERT   Pint please, Maisie.
(*Pint pulled.*)

ALBERT   Ta love. Aah, just 'job. (*pause*) Sid! Heyup lad.

SID   Hello Albert.

ALBERT   You look as though you've lost a bob and found a tanner — you need a drink — 'nother pint please Maisie —
(*Pint pulled.*)

ALBERT   Ta. There you are lad, now get that down you, make you feel better.

SID   Cheers Albert. (*Rattle Rattle*)

ALBERT   Drink it Sid, don't gargle with it, it's not a bloody mouthwash.

SID   Sorry Albert, can't help it. (*Rattle Rattle*)

ALBERT   Ee, I don't know, Sid. You're just not yourself. You've not been right for days. In thirty years of our being on 'committee together, I've never known you go off like you did on Sunday.

SID   Aye, I know. Listen, Albert you and me, we go back a long way, don't we?

ALBERT   We do that.

SID   Aye, well I've got summat to tell you, but keep it quiet. Nobody else knows yet, not even my family. Ee, I've got to tell someone though, it's preying on my mind that much....

ALBERT   Go on then.

SID   I am slowly turning into a giant beetle.

ALBERT   A beetle? What sort of beetle?

SID   A cockroach.

ALBERT   What?

SID   Or *Periplaneta Americana* to give me my scientific name. Not even a native English beetle at that — some bloody foreign species.

ALBERT   How do you know you are?

SID   Here — anybody looking? No? Right, just take a look at this arm. I'll lift the front of 'sling up a bit...there...see.

ALBERT   Aye, you're right, kid. Can't doctor give you owt for it?

SID   Actually Albert, I told you a little white lie at 'meeting. I haven't been to 'doctor's. I'm scared to. I've been down to 'library, been reading a few text books, see. Listen to this bit: '*Periplaneta Americana* is, because of its size, the one usually selected for practical examination'. If I go into that bloody surgery, I'll not be coming out, I'll be laid out on a dissecting board with pins stuck in me chest. (*Rattle Rattle*)

ALBERT   You seem to know a lot about 'subject.

SID   Aye, well it's in my own interests, isn't it?

ALBERT   Aye.

SID   Listen to what else 'book says: 'Cockroaches are omnivorous insects, feeding on scraps of food and other organic matter like wool, fluff or even paper' — bloody appetising that — 'The creature is principally nocturnal in its habits' — won't be getting much sleep from now on either. Now where was I, ah yes — 'All species have been introduced into this country from elsewhere, probably via the holds of cargo ships'. Charming, eh, not only a beetle but a bloody illegal immigrant an' all.

ALBERT   Hey, how quick is it happening then?

SID   Yer what?

ALBERT   This changing into a beetle?

SID   Well I'm not sure exactly. I first noticed it last week — my left hand started going brown and getting all pointed-like, then I started getting these thick stiff hairs growing out of my left arm, and yesterday, I started sprouting another 'un.

ALBERT Another what?

SID A third arm. It's not very big yet, but it's grown six inches in two days. I reckon at 'current rate of progress I'll be completely transformed by end o' month at 'latest.

ALBERT What's your missus going to say?

SID Ee, I don't know. She'll probably go off to her sister's. I'm trying to pluck up 'courage to tell her. Here, let's have another pint shall we. (*Rattle Rattle*)

ALBERT Aye, I reckon you need one....
(*Fade out.*)
(*Fade in Sid's house.*)

DORA (*off*) Dinner's ready. Your Dad in yet?

ERIC Nah, Mam, he's not back from 'club yet — not like him to be late for his Saturday dinner.

DORA Ee, I don't know, he's just not himself at all. He used to be regular as clockwork in his habits — you could set your watch by him — an' he used to be so gentle, but he's that bad tempered now!

ERIC Aye, I know Mam. I've had to stop bringing Sharon round in case he gives her a mouthful, it's not right you know.

DORA I know, love. Hey, here he is coming up 'garden. Now don't go saying anything to upset him.

SID Hello Dora, hello Eric.

DORA You're late Sid, but never mind love, it's your favourite for dinner, steak and kidney pie with onion gravy. Come and sit at 'table now.

SID I, oh, er.... I'm not all that hungry really. (*Rattle Rattle*)

ERIC Not hungry? It's the first time I've ever heard you say that Dad.

DORA I suppose you'll be leaving your overcoat on, as usual?

ERIC No he's not, I'm not sitting through another

      meal watching him dangle his sleeves in gravy pot and dripping all over tablecloth. It's making me sick — that overcoat is coming off!

DORA No, Eric don't....(*rip*)

ERIC Oh.

DORA Sid, love.

SID Well, I were hoping to break it to you a bit gentler like but seeing as you've forced my hand.

ERIC Ugh!

DORA What's happening to you?

SID (*resigned*) I am slowly turning into a giant beetle.

DORA What sort of beetle?

SID *Periplaneta Americana.*

ERIC Peri what?

SID Or to give me my common name, a cockroach.

ERIC Ugh!

DORA You'd better sit down in 'front room and have an aspirin, love....

ERIC It's not catching is it?

SID I don't think so, lad. Yer Mam's not turned into a ladybird yet.

ERIC Hey, it might be hereditary though. Bloody hell! I might turn into a beetle! Or worse, my Sharon might give birth to one. I can just see me going into maternity ward and asking 'sister, is it a boy, a girl or a beetle? I want to produce heirs to join in running the business — Arkwright and Sons, not a bloody menagerie. Here, I'm off.

DORA Where are you going love?

ERIC I'm getting myself off to outpatients' for a checkup, I'm not taking any chances.
(*Door bangs.*)

DORA What'd you have to go upsetting our Eric like that for? You know he's a bit on edge at 'moment with 'wedding coming up. Hey, what you doing with my knitting? You're not eating it are you?

SID Well, I'm starving love. (*Rattle Rattle*)
(*Fade out.*)

(*Fade in committee meeting.*)

ALBERT Right, gentlemen, I call this special meeting of committee to order. As you know, I've called meeting to discuss a (ahem) little problem that our Sid's been having....

SID (*Rattle Rattle*)

ALBERT ....and er, see if there's owt we can do to help him out in his predicament.

HARRY What's crack then Albert?

ALBERT Alright Sid, unveil your arm.

SID Righto Albert, but it's arms actually. (*Rattle Rattle*)

FRED Bloody hell, he's got three of 'buggers, all brown and stubbly.

SID Aye, and there's another on't way — look, only two inches long at 'moment but I reckon it'll be full size by Tuesday afternoon.

ALBERT As you can see lads, our Sid's turning into a giant cockroach.

FRED How you feeling Sid? I mean, you look quite well on it.

SID Aye, alright I suppose. Actually, looking on 'bright side, this new exoskeleton's improved my bad back no end.

HARRY But what can we do about it Albert?

ALBERT Well, I thought maybe arrange a few fund-raising events, you know, to enable us to send Sid to a specialist, maybe a private clinic in Switzerland or summat.

SID Albert, lad, I've already told you — no doctors!

FRED Well, how about an ocean cruise then? A change of air might prove beneficial, Sid. All that ozone, lots of sun, sea and deck tennis — just what you need. Do you a world of good.

HARRY Hey up, wait a minute, it's not catching is it?

SID No it's not, that's just a common misconception about this condition. I'm very grateful for your concern though, er (*Rattle Rattle, cough*) sorry, just a frog in my throat.

HARRY	Didn't know cockroaches ate frogs. Har, har.
ALBERT	Shut up Harry! Now, any suggestions on how we're going to raise this money!
FRED	How about a beetle drive?
ALBERT	Fred.
FRED	Sorry, weren't thinking.
ALBERT	Aye well, we'll come up with something I expect. Now Sid, you sure you'll be all right to perform Concert Chairman's duties tomorrow.
SID	Aye, I'll be champion. (*Rattle Rattle*) (*Fade out.*) (*Fade in background chatter and clink of glasses..*)
SID	Thank you, ladies and gentlemen, and now your draw for your members' tote. Thank you Fred.
FRED	Thank you Sid.
SID	And the winning number is (*Rattle Rattle*).
VOICE	What were that?
SID	238
VOICE	(*disappointed*) Oh.
SID	And now to continue your entertainment, we have your artiste, a marvellous magician and great local favourite (*Rattle Rattle Rattle*).
VOICE	What's that, Sid, taken up yodelling?
SID	Let's have some order please — thank you — your artiste for tonight, a very big welcome for (*Rattle Rattle Rattle*).
VOICE	Get on with it.
VOICE	Sounds like bathwater going down plughole.
ALBERT	(*forced whisper*) Stop larking about and get that turn on, Sid. They'll be coming up for't bingo soon from t'estate.
SID	(*to Albert*) Sorry, Albert (*Rattle*). (*through microphone*) Thank you ladies and gentlemen, please welcome El Magico and The Lovely Maureen (*Rattle Rattle*).
VOICE	Hey up, it's them bloody flamenco dancers we had last week!
SID	Shut up! He's a top artist, this lad (*Rattle Rattle*).

109

	He can do owt! Best of order please for El Magico!
EL MAGICO	(*fake Spanish accent*) Thank you, ladies and gentlemen, thank you. And now, magic that will feast your eyes and leave you gasping with amazement. I will now transport you with just a wave of my magic wand from, er....Westhorpe Social Club to the land of Let's Pretend. Music maestro, please....!
	(*Taped music starts up.*)
EL MAGICO	(*fake Spanish accent*) Now, if the lovely Maureen would pass me my magic deck of cards....
	(*Maureen whispers to him.*)
EL MAGICO	(*broad Lancashire accent*) What do you mean, they aren't in the trunk?
MAUREEN	Sorry.
EL MAGICO	(*sotto voce*) Never mind, get the 'at. (*fake Spanish accent*) And now, the lovely Maureen will pass me my magic top hat. As you can see, this appears to be a perfectly ordinary top hat.
EL MAGICO	(*knocking hat*) Completely empty inside. But.... just one tap from my magic wand and — hey presto!
	(*Cooing noises followed by flapping and crashing.*)
EL MAGICO	(*broad Lancashire accent*) Bugger me!
MAUREEN	Oooh, that hurt!
ALBERT	Bloody 'ell, Sid's sprouted wings and crash-landed into 'turn.
	(*Hubbub*)
ALBERT	(*through microphone*) Your attention please, ladies and gentlemen. Thank you very much. El Magico will be back with you as soon as he's, er, mended his wand. So in 'meantime we'll get straight on to your bingo.
VOICE 1	That's more like it.
VOICE 2	Aye.
ALBERT	Eyes down, please, for your first house. Thank you Fred.
FRED	Thank you Albert and your first number is....
	(*Fade out.*)

(*Fade in committee meeting.*)

ALBERT   Right lads, let's come to order shall we? Now, er, following last night's performance.

HARRY   Aye, an' a right bloody performance it were an all.

ALBERT   This special meeting of the committee has been convened by Harry. I suppose you've got the requisite number of signatures Harry?

HARRY   More than enough. People are up in arms about it — never been known, and Sid, take your cap off in 'committee room, 'specially when it's you that's being discussed.

SID   I'd like to lads, but it's my antennae, they'd stick up like chapel hat pegs. (*Rattle Rattle*) And they're right tender an' all. They'd start itching in this smoky atmosphere, so if you don't mind, I'll keep it on.

ALBERT   Right, then, can we please get down to the business of this meeting, which is, ahem, I regret, to relieve Sid of his duties as Concert Chairman.

SID   (*Rattle Rattle*)

FRED   Hang on a minute, shouldn't we discuss it first. I mean it's not cut and dried is it?

HARRY   Course it bloody is! It's a foregone conclusion after last night's debacle.

ALBERT   Aye Sid, there was no need to dive-bomb t'artiste like that.

SID   I couldn't help it, my wings suddenly started flapping and I couldn't stop 'em. How is he anyway?

ALBERT   Oh, he'll be alright. He agreed not to prefer charges — after we offered him double his normal fee.

FRED   Look Sid, perhaps you didn't like him personally but as Concert Chairman you're supposed to be impartial. Can't you try and control your temper?

SID   It's not a question of temper with us beetles, it's instinct. When we get agitated we start flapping our wings. It's called 'flight or fight response'.

ALBERT   Aye, well, to put it in perspective, Sid, from now on we're going to have to treat you like we treat t'other socially suspect minority groups, like skinheads and lefties, we'll let you in 'club if you behave yourself, but any sign of trouble and you're out — fair enough?

SID   (*Rattle Rattle*)

ALBERT   Right, then, let's take vote on 'proposition that Sid be relieved of his duties as Concert Chairman as from today. All those in favour.

HARRY)
FRED)   Aye.
ALBERT)

ALBERT   Against?

SID   (*Rattle Rattle*)

HARRY   You can't vote on your own censure motion, Sid.

SID   I wasn't voting. I was just rattling.

ALBERT   Carried then, unanimous, and try and stay in tap room Sid, we don't want them young lasses in 'lounge frightening to death.

(*Fade out. Fade in knives and forks on plates*)

DORA   Eat up your Yorkshire Pud, Sid! You used to say I made best Yorkshires in Yorkshire: you once told me you only married me for my Yorkshires....

SID   Happen I did. (*Rattle Rattle*) I'm just not very hungry today, that's all.

ERIC   Aye. It's only 'cos you've been chewing bloody wallpaper in 'sitting room all morning — and don't think I didn't see you — no wonder it's all peeling off.

DORA   Sid!

ERIC   Come on Dad, stop playing this silly game! You've put me and me mam through enough misery these past few days. Give it a rest.

SID   I am not playing games. I am turning into a

giant cockroach, or had you forgotten?

ERIC   Forgotten? How could I forget? It's all you ever talk about!

SID   It's a very interesting subject you know, I've been reading all about myself in this textbook. Look, there's a few pages missing of course where I've had a quick bite or two, but there's a good bit here, all about the details of my anatomical structure.

DORA   Sid! We don't want to know.

ERIC   No we don't, makes my flesh crawl, all that stuff.

DORA   Why don't you try and get out more, Sid — take your mind off it. You're making 'sitting room smell stale, spending all day stretched out on 'floor under 'settee.

SID   But it's my natural habitat: we like warm, dark sheltered places. Anyway, I'm fed up with being stared at in 'street, anybody'd think folk round here'd never seen a beetle before!

DORA   So you don't want these Yorkshires then.

SID   Well, I could make a little nest out of them, I suppose, when they've dried up....

DORA   Oh Sid....(*tears*)

(*Fade out.*)

(*Fade in.*)

DORA   Sid, stop scuttling about and listen to me a minute.

SID   (*Rattle Rattle Rattle*)

DORA   You've always liked pottering about in't shed, haven't you? Well, I've put a nice camp bed in there, with a little paraffin heater. You'll be lovely and warm and I've boarded 'windows up so it'll be dark enough for you. I'll put you out a fresh bucket of t'emptyings from 'vacuum cleaner every day. They're you're favourite, aren't they?

SID   (*Rattle Rattle*)

DORA   'Cos I'm afraid I can't stand you any more, not even in't same room. I mean, your body odour's getting worse — you're starting to smell you know. I can't even bear 'thought of using same loo as you. So, you can use that outside one from now on. If Eric hears that you've moved into t'shed he might come back. You do realise it's three days since he went and we haven't heard a word from him?

SID   (*Rattle Rattle*)

DORA   Aye, that's all you can do — rattle. Well you can rattle to your heart's content in that shed, can't you?
(*Fade out.*)
(*Fade in committee meeting.*)

ALBERT   Right, any other business?

HARRY   Aye, is there any point in having a beetle on 'committee? Sid just sits there now rattlin' on all time. He can't contribute owt, you might as well have a bloody budgie on 'committee.

ALBERT   Aye, but Sid's been on 'committee nigh on thirty years.

HARRY   Aye, I'm aware of that, but all of us on committee are good old-fashioned Yorkshire lads — not beetles, especially not foreign beetles — we're meant to be representatives for 'whole club. Sid's only representing himself and that's plain selfish, there's no other beetles in 'club to my knowledge.

FRED   I'm afraid Harry's got a point there, Albert, it'd be cruel to keep him on in a position of responsibility when he's unable to play his full part any longer.

ALBERT   Aye, I think I'm in agreement with you. All in favour of Sid being asked to resign from committee?

HARRY)
FRED)   Aye.
ALBERT)

ALBERT   Carried unanimous.
(*Fade out, fade in.*)

DORA   Sid! Can you hear me? I know you're in there.

SID   (*Rattle Rattle*)

DORA   Sid! I'm really disgusted with you. I told you to stay in that shed. Are you trying to break up our home, or what?

SID   (*Rattle Rattle*)

DORA   You know what I'm talking about Sid Arkwright, I've found your tracks all throughout house to 'bathroom and then all them scales in 'bath. You tried to have a bath didn't you? It's horrible. Anyway that's 'last straw. I'm having 'locks changed this afternoon, and I'm getting in touch with 'lawyer. I'm going for a divorce Sid — mental cruelty — my life's been hell these last few weeks. Well, I'm not having any more of it, you can stay in that shed or you can come out. I don't care, but you're not coming back into my house and that's final.

SID   (*Rattle Rattle*)
        (*Fade out.*)
        (*Fade in committee meeting.*)

ALBERT   Right, let's get this over with shall we.

HARRY   Aye, all those in favour of 'motion.

ALBERT   Hang about, Harry, I've not read it out yet.

HARRY   Just get on with it.

ALBERT   We've got to follow correct procedures. Now then, Harry has brought to my notice 'clause in club rules that states that no animals be allowed in the club except guide dogs for the blind.

FRED   Aye, Sid proposed that himself.

ALBERT   Right, that being the case, and as Sid is clearly now completely turned into a cockroach, we've no option but to suspend his membership. All those in favour?

FRED)
HARRY)   Aye.
ALBERT)

ALBERT   Carried unanimous. I'll nip round to his house and reclaim his card.
        (*Fade out.*)

(*Fade in shed. A cock crows.*)

SID   (*yawning*) I wish he'd sell them bloody chickens, waking me up every morning. Brr, it's cold in this shed. What time is it? (*repeats to himself*) What time is it? Hey, I'm talking proper again — 'How now brown cow' — 'Peter Piper picked a peck of pickled pepper' — Hey, spot on — not a single rattle — and my arms, my legs, hey, I'm back to normal, I've got my hair back — no antennae! I'm Sid Arkwright again! Dora! (*louder*) Dora!

(*Running footsteps, knocking on door.*)

SID   Dora! Let me in! It's Sid, I'm back to normal, Dora! Come down and open the door, it's Sid! Listen, I've changed back, it's alright now, I'm not a beetle any more.

(*More knocking on door.*)

SID   Open the door. Come on.

(*Sound of door being rattled forcibly.*)

SID   Ouch, my bad back.

DORA   (*off*) What's all that racket about down there?

SID   It's me love — Sid — look, I'm me old self again.

DORA   (*off*) Oh, bloody 'ell.

SID   Well are you going to let me in or not then? I'm bloody freezing out here. I haven't got my protective cuticle to keep out 'cold now you know.

DORA   Er, just a minute, love. Er, don't go away —

SID   Don't go away, she says, don't know what's up with her. Anybody'd think....

(*Door unlocked and opened.*)

ALBERT   Morning Sid.

SID   Albert, what are....

ALBERT   You'd best come in.

SID   (*perplexed*) Aye.

ALBERT   Sit yourself down, lad. I'll mash some tea.

SID   Albert...

ALBERT   I'm right glad to see you back to summat like your old self again, Sid lad, but there's some-

116

thing you've got to know.

SID But....

ALBERT Don't say owt, just listen. Your Dora's been put right through it these last few weeks. She's been desperate Sid — she had to turn to someone — so I've been coming round now and again, you know, just to cheer her up and keep her company.

SID At seven o'clock in 'bloody morning?

ALBERT Aye, I know how it looks, Sid, but Dora's been getting all nervous about being in 'house by herself these past few nights with Eric gone. So I've been spending 'nights here on 'settee like.

DORA Morning Sid.

SID Dora, love.

DORA You'd better stop beating about 'bush, Albert and tell Sid 'truth.

SID What do you mean, what truth?

DORA I'm a woman Sid, I need a man, I can't live with a beetle for the rest of my life. So, as soon as 'divorce comes through I'm setting up house with Albert here. I'm sorry, Sid, but I've got me own life to think about.

SID But look at me, Dora love, I'm not a beetle any more — I'm completely changed back, I'm your old Sid again. Look at me, will you! Dora, everything can be just like it was.

ALBERT I'm afraid it's not quite as straightforward as that.

DORA No Sid, you might appear normal on 'surface, but who's to know this isn't only a temporary respite. It might be a recurring condition, I couldn't take 'risk. I'd be worrying about it every bloody day, every morning, waking up not knowing if I'm in bed with a man or a beetle. I couldn't go through it all again, I'm sorry Sid, I've made me mind up.

SID Dora.

ALBERT It's a shame you had to hear it like this Sid. We

were going to leave you a little note, but we weren't sure if cockroaches could read or not.

DORA But we wouldn't want to kick you out into 'street. You can kip in spare room – until you find somewhere suitable.

SID (*angrily*) Bloody hell, to be treated like this in my own house and after all I've gone through. Well I'm not sitting here, having breakfast with you two all lovey-dovey in my kitchen. I'm off down 'transport cafe where 'company's a bit better. Ta ra!

(*Slams door, fade out.*)

(*Fade in committee meeting.*)

ALBERT Shall we make a start then, lads?

HARRY Well we've got a quorum, I think, Albert.

ALBERT Right then, the question before 'committee is Sid Arkwright's request to be reinstated back into 'club and back onto 'committee on account of his not being a beetle any more.

HARRY How do we know?

ALBERT How do we know what?

HARRY How do we know he's not a beetle any more.

FRED I've seen him, Harry, he's completely back to his old self — not a trace of beetle about him. It's the Sid we've known and respected for thirty years, back with us again.

HARRY Aye, but you know what they say.

ALBERT What?

HARRY Once a cockroach, always a cockroach.

FRED Harry! That were only a temporary medical condition, he's right as rain again now.

ALBERT But can you be sure, Fred? It might come back. I know a bloke who's had malaria once every two years, regular as clockwork, ever since war!

HARRY He'll always have it in his blood. It's not in 'best interests of club to take that sort of risk.

FRED Aye, maybe there's summat in what you say, Harry.

HARRY	Too right there is.
FRED	Of course, if it were just us to consider that would be a different kettle of fish entirely. I mean we're Sid's mates....
ALBERT	Aye, but there's not just us to consider is there? We've been voted into this position of respect and responsibility to look after 'club and its members, we've got to repay 'trust that's been placed in us and with elections coming up we don't want to rock the boat, do we?
FRED	I suppose you're right, Albert.
HARRY	Course he is. Let's vote on it then, shall we?
ALBERT	All right then, all those in favour of not rein-stating Sid back into 'club?
ALBERT) FRED) HARRY)	Aye!
ALBERT	Carried unanimous. He's waiting on us downstairs in 'snack bar. Fred, better go and tell him our decision. (*Fade out, fade in snack bar.*)
SID	Can we have a bit of service down here?
ADA	Yes?
SID	What have you got then? Let me have a look.... steakwich, pie and peas, cornish pasty.... Hey —
ADA	What?
SID	You wouldn't happen to have a nice bowl of sawdust would you?
ADA	Eh?
SID	I mean.... pie and peas, please love.... (*pause*) Hey up Fred! Ee, it's grand to be back in 'club. What's verdict then? (*Fade out.*)

Follow On

The aim of the activities in this section is to add to students' enjoyment and understanding of the five plays in this anthology. Some plays students may simply wish to act out in class or perform on stage, others may be discussed and written about and some may stimulate their own playwriting.

Some of the Follow On suggestions are based on developing the text, such as writing additional scenes or alternative endings, and some are based on imitating the text, such as relocating the characters in other situations. All the Follow On activities involve a mixture of individual, group and whole class work and can be used to help students build up a coursework folder for the General Certificate of Secondary Education in English, English Literature and Drama.

*H*ome

UNDERSTANDING THE PLAY

CAN YOU think of any other appropriate and interesting titles for this play?

IN 'RADIO DRAMA' William Ash writes:

> *The radio playwright must never forget that the audience is blind without ever making them feel for a moment that they are. The dialogue of a radio play has to set the stage, provide all the props, describe and costume the characters, change the scenes and bring down the final curtain without ever seeming to do anything but advance the dramatic story.*

> From *The Way To Write Radio Drama* by William Ash
> published by Elm Tree Books, London, 1985.

How far do you think 'Home' measures up to this description of the 'good' radio drama?

WOULD THE events have been any different if Alan's child had been a son rather than a daughter? Give reasons.

IN WHAT ways does Berlie Doherty highlight Lisa's loneliness and unhappiness? Try to sum up in your own words how Lisa feels.

ARE THERE any parts of the play which do not seem convincing to you or which you feel could be cut out or improved? Make notes of any changes you feel are needed and discuss them with a partner.

IF YOU got the opportunity of meeting Berlie Doherty what questions would you ask her about this play?

IDEAS FOR DISCUSSION AND IMPROVISATION

'HOME' EXPLORES the relationship between a daughter and her father and stepmother. Was the conflict which developed inevitable? What caused the trouble? Discuss with a partner.

IN GROUPS discuss your reactions to the following:

Claire never talks to me, Dad. She's so nice to me when you're here, but when you're not ... I wish you knew. (Lisa)

I wish I'd never come back here. It's different. You're different. (Lisa)

Teenagers always like to stay in their own rooms. I did. (Claire)

She's like a ghost the way she walks round the house all day ... She won't talk to me ... she just shrugs when I speak to her. She won't do a thing to help round the house unless I ask her to. (Claire)

You have to make allowances for her. (Alan)

I wish you wouldn't be so difficult, Lisa. (Alan)

With whom do you sympathise most?

IMPROVISE SHORT scenes based on one of the following statements made by a parent to a son or daughter:

Just look at the state of those clothes!

And what time do you call this?

Your bedroom is like a rubbish tip!

I'm not made of money you know!

I don't want you hanging about with the likes of him/her.

UNLIKE THE novelist the radio dramatist cannot describe the appearances of the characters except through the words they use. Discuss in pairs or in groups how you think the three characters in this play look. What clues have you found in the script to help you visualise Lisa, Alan and Claire?

IDEAS FOR WRITING

WRITE A preview of 'Home' for the Radio Times in which you give a brief outline of the plot.

IF YOU were preparing to present this drama on stage what changes and additions would be necessary?

TRY WRITING some scenes that might have taken place but did not appear in the script. For example:
– Alan and Claire's conversation on finding Lisa has gone
– Lisa's explanation to her mother when she leaves home
– Claire's account of the events to a friend
– a meeting between Alan and his daughter two weeks later when Lisa comes to collect her belongings
– a telephone call in which Alan tries to explain matters to his former wife.

WRITE YOUR own story, play or poem about a young person who leaves home and, after a period of time away, returns.

WRITE A poem in response to 'Home'. It may be about a character or an event or written from the point of view of one of the characters.

IN THE play Lisa writes her thoughts down in a series of letters to her father. Suppose Lisa had written to her mother describing her life with Alan and Claire and her mother had replied. Write the letters they might have exchanged. An alternative would be to write the letter Lisa might have sent to a magazine problem page with the reply.

IT IS often difficult to bring a drama to a satisfying conclusion. Do you feel Berlie Doherty is successful? Write an alternative scene to end the play.

WRITE YOUR own radio play called 'Two's Company, Three's a Crowd'. Your script should be for three characters, one of whom is the 'outsider' who has a powerful effect on the other two. Before you start, read the following advice by a script editor:

> *One of the commonest faults in the radio drama written by those new to this medium is simply that it is not dramatic enough. There may be quite a good story or plot line and some interestingly conceived characters but it fails to make dramatic capital out of the possibilities of conflict and confrontation implicit in the play. It is all too easy in radio drama for the actors, whom we cannot see, to turn back into narrators and start telling us about what has happened instead of acting it out for us. The injuction to all dramatists, 'Don't tell us; show us', must be addressed with an even greater cogency to radio dramatists.*

> From *The Way To Write Radio Drama* by William Ash
> published by Elm Tree Books, London, 1985.

The following ten suggestions for laying out a radio script may be helpful:

1 Give yourself a wide margin of about one third of the width of the paper. This will be for the speakers' names and any rough production notes.

2 Everything which is not spoken should be underlined.

3 Write speakers' names in capital letters.

4 FX indicates sound effect.

5 A radio adaptation is only sound. Don't write 'Sunlight lit up the whole room'.

6 Avoid using too many characters.

7 Avoid using a narrator, but if you must, make what he or she has to say clear and brief.

8 Sound effects can be used for the setting of the drama: a noisy school corridor, street sounds, country noises etc.

9 There is greater freedom on radio to use a lot of scenes. The writer is not limited to a few sets as in a television play.

10 Scenes begin and end with fading. Music could be used to begin and end your adaptation.

When the script is completed select a producer, nominate a pupil to be in charge of sound effects, and assign parts to the actresses and actors. After a few rehearsals you will be ready to record your play.

Keep On Running

UNDERSTANDING THE PLAY

IN PAIRS read Roger Burford-Mason's introduction to his play. What does it add to your appreciation of 'Keep On Running'?

WHAT DEVICES does Roger Burford-Mason employ in the play to create the tense atmosphere?

DISCUSS THE way in which the relationship between Jackie and her parents has been portrayed. Do any of the scenes involving these three characters seem to you unreal or very true to life?

HERE ARE two statements about the ending of 'Keep On Running':
– the dream sequence spoils an otherwise excellent piece of drama
– the ending is most effective, there are no neat and tidy solutions and it keeps us guessing.
With which do you agree? Can you think of any alternative conclusions to the play?

IDEAS FOR DISCUSSION AND IMPROVISATION

BELOW ARE a number of statements made by characters in the play. In groups discuss their views:

Your real life is here with your family or out having a laugh with your friends. Boyfriends. Getting married. Having a home. That's real life. (Jackie's father)

Girls have got the same rights as boys to go as far and do as well as they can. (Miss Bell)

See it from my point of view. I know what's best for me. (Jackie)

You've got to believe in something, Jackie. If you believe in something enough you'll do the right thing. (Woman at end)

THE MAIN characters in this play give away clues about themselves as the story unfolds. Look at what Jackie's parents say and discuss what sort of characters they are. Write a paragraph describing each.

126

BELOW ARE a selection of opinions about aspects of the play from teachers and students:
– Kevin is attractive and odious at the same time, and the gradual way in which he wins Jackie from her running is a source of real tension in the script
– the most convincing adult character is Miss Bell
– the play is too serious and gloomy; a bit of humour would have been welcome
– Jackie's various dilemmas and conflicts are presented without false sentiment, nor with any attempt to trivialise what could be real concerns for a girl of this kind.
In groups discuss these views. With which do you agree?

THINK ABOUT the last time you disagreed with one of your parents. What were your thoughts and feelings at the time and what did you actually say and do?

IDEAS FOR WRITING

WRITE A brief outline of the plot, a synopsis of about two hundred words.

THINK OF a time when you were faced, like Jackie, with a difficult decision and received conflicting advice on what to do. Describe that occasion. You might write your story in the form of a narrative or a play.

IN PAIRS decide on the dramatic high points of the play. Write out one dramatic scene as prose.

THE RADIO dramatist, unlike the novelist, cannot describe the appearances of the various characters. We only learn about them through the things they say. How do you visualise Jackie, Glynnis, Miss Bell and Kevin? Write a paragraph on each.

IMAGINE JACKIE keeps a diary recording, amongst other things, details of her running activities. Write several entries including one for the night before the National Finals at Brighton.

IMAGINE JACKIE competes in the National Finals at Brighton. Write the description of the race in the form of a sports' commentary.

IN THIS poem a fifth year student describes her experience of school sports, which is very different from Jackie's.

All Fun And Games

I disliked games at school!
All that 'jolly hockeysticks' and sweat,
All that 'All pals together'
'Working as a team',
'Pulling in the same direction'
The only things I pulled were muscles.

I disliked games at school!
Netball and lacrosse,
Tennis and squash.
I hated hockey with those stocky, he-men girls,
All muscle and mouth.
I loathed lacrosse with those
Bony, big-booted, Boadiceas
Bombing down the pitch.
I abhorred netball with those
nine-foot Amazons,
Knocking your knees and jumping
on your feet.

Games for me meant:
scrapes and scratches, aches and pains,
fear and failure.
And I was never any good!

Jayne Pearce

Write two poems, one about an interest or hobby which you very much enjoy and another about an activity or task which you really dislike.

JACKIE IS interviewed for an article about her running achievements for the school magazine. Write either the interview or the article.

TRY WRITING some of the scenes the playwright did not include, for example:
– the telephone conversation when Jackie's mum explains to Aunty Betty why the weekend in Norfolk has to be cancelled
– the night of the disco when Kevin takes Glynnis
– Miss Bell's interview with Jackie's parents when she tries to persuade them to support their daughter's passion for running
– the conversation in the pub where Jackie's father tells his mates about his daughter's 'hare-brained' schemes.

Follow On

HERE IS a report slip for Jackie's school:

Subject .... Ability .... Effort ....

Teacher ....

Using the information contained in the play, complete reports for several of the subjects Jackie takes.

THE PLAY ends with Jackie's dilemma: 'What shall I do?' Write an additional scene describing the decision she makes.

SOME YEARS later Jackie describes her teenage years to her daughter with all the tensions and pressures and the joys and successes. Write her account as a monologue.

*A*udition

UNDERSTANDING THE PLAY

LOOK CAREFULLY at the directions at the beginning of the play. How important are these in setting the scene and creating the atmosphere?

WHY DO you think Alma Cullen chose 'The Crucible' as the school play?

EXPLAIN WHY Rachel refuses to face up to the fact of her mother's pregnancy. Have you ever tried to block out a problem or worry in your life?

WHEN WE describe someone's personality we frequently pick out the main characteristics. Rachel is described as lacking in maturity by Barney and 'a pain in the bum sometimes' by Kim. Briefly say how you would describe Rachel. Why was she unsuitable for the part of Abigail?

WHAT DEVICES does the playwright use in this play to highlight Rachel's unhappiness and anxiety and to build up the tension between Rachel and her parents?

HOW DO Rachel's attitudes change during the play? Explain what events affect them.

WHAT DO you imagine will happen to Rachel and her family during the next four weeks?

IDEAS FOR DISCUSSION AND IMPROVISATION

THAT EVENING Kevin, unaware that he has been seen with another girl, calls on Kim. Improvise the scene.

BELOW ARE some statements about the play. Working in pairs choose those with which you agree and explain why:
- Barney Grant is too close to caricature to be credible
- Kim provides some contrast to Rachel, although her part is too short to allow much development to take place

– the relationship between Rachel and her family is explored realistically and sensitively
– the strength of this play is in the strong characterisation
– things would have been very different if it had been a teenage son rather than daughter, having to come to terms with the situation.

AT THE very end Rachel says 'And then I'll ring Kim'. In pairs simulate the telephone call.

WHAT EFFECT does Alma Cullen achieve in ending the play as she does? Discuss alternative endings.

IDEAS FOR WRITING

BEFORE A play appears on the television screen, auditions take place. Actors and actresses have to be found who look and sound right and understand how the various characters feel and think. Imagine you are the Casting Director. Devise portraits of the central characters as you imagine them to be.

THE ACTION in 'Audition' centres on the events of one particular day. Imagine Rachel had kept a diary. Write the entry for this day.

RACHEL IS bitterly disappointed when she fails to get the part. Write a poem about a time when you have been disappointed.

TELL PART of Rachel's story in the form of a comic strip. You might work with a partner, one as the artist and the other the 'bubble' writer.

RACHEL FEELS angry and upset when Barney Grant 'shows her up' in class. Comment on his treatment of her. Describe your thoughts and feelings on an occasion when you have felt humiliated or embarrassed.

'I DON'T even know if I *want* another baby,' says Mrs. Hammond. Write the letter she might have sent to a magazine problem page asking for advice as to whether she should have the baby or not. Write the reply.

WRITE A short television script based on a true incident at home or in school.

The following series of suggestions for the layout of your script may be helpful:

1 Use only the right-hand side of the paper, leaving space for the producer to make notes.

2 Speakers' names, directions and descriptions are all written in capitals. Only the actual words spoken are written in lower case.

3 Do not include too much dialogue. Television, unlike radio, is visual and facial expressions can often make dialogue unnecessary.

4 Do not use too many characters. Television is a medium which uses close-ups.

5 The characters and their relationships with others must be clearly established.

6 Scenes should be kept to a minimum. A main feature of the television drama is that speedy transitions from one scene to another can be made. It can also include travel scenes, for example scenes where characters take a train journey or walk through a city.

Replay For A Plumber

UNDERSTANDING THE PLAY

WHAT DO you think will happen to Bert in the next ten years? Will he continue to have premonitions?

WITH A partner identify those parts of the play you feel work well and hold the audience's interest.

HOW DO you think you would have behaved had you been in a similar situation to Bert or Mrs. Brady-Smith?

COMPARE THE lifestyles of Bert and Mrs. Brady-Smith.

IDEAS FOR DISCUSSION AND IMPROVISATION

BELOW IS a list of statements about the play by teachers. In groups discuss each comment and decide on those with which you agree.

I am not very happy about the exploding paper, merely because many of the students reading this play would reject that notion as being highly implausible.

From a construction point of view this is by far the most interesting of the five plays.

The ending is superb, where events turn full circle.

I found the ending rather predictable but youngsters would probably enjoy it.

IN SMALL groups record this play for radio. The question of staging does not arise but you will need to consider sound effects and elements of speech (stress, tone, volume, pace, articulation, accent).

FOLLOWING THE death of Edward and the disappearance of Peter, the Board of Directors of Quality Papers Ltd. meets to discuss the situation. Improvise the scene.

BERT SAYS, 'You know the feeling. As though you'd done it before.' What he describes is déjà vu, an illusion of experiencing something which happened some time in the past.
Discuss in groups any experiences of déjà vu you have had or

133

heard about. Make a collection either on tape or in a booklet or for a wall display.

AFTER THE explosion Mrs. Brady-Smith tells her story to the police. Improvise or write out the interview which takes place.

DEVISE A mock trial in which Peter Brady-Smith appears, accused of terrorism and murder.
You might wish to use the following sequence for the case:

– Peter Brady-Smith is charged by the *Clerk of the Court* and pleads either guilty or not guilty

– the *Prosecution* outlines the facts of the case

– the *Prosecution* calls its witnesses: the investigating police officer, neighbours and Bert Addley

– the *Defence Counsel* cross-examines the witnesses on the evidence they have just given

– the *Defence* opens its case and calls the defence witnesses: work colleagues of the defendant, his secretary, Peter Brady-Smith (the defendant)

– the *Prosecution* cross-examines these witnesses

– the *Defence* summarises its case and urges the jury to return a verdict of 'Not Guilty'

– the *Prosecution* concludes its case and asks for a verdict of 'Guilty'

– the *Judge* sums up the trial, reviewing the evidence and pointing out any inconsistencies

– the *Jury* retire and, under the direction of the *Foreman* or *Forewoman*, considers its verdict

– the *Jury* returns, the verdict is pronounced and the *Judge* delivers sentence.

IDEAS FOR WRITING

REWRITE THE opening scene of the play in prose, fleshing out the dialogue with details and descriptions.

WRITE A character study of Bert.

USING THE events in the play write a television or radio news report about the explosion.

IN THIS poem a fifth year student describes the scene after an explosion:

> Number Nineteen was a small house,
> A neat and nondescript sort of place,
> A little box of red bricks,
> With a grey slate roof,
> Square windows and a tidy garden,
> It once was ...
>
> Number Nineteen is a mound of smoking rubble now,
> A black and broken pile of bricks,
> with a shroud of grey dust and splintered glass
> covering all,
> Deep holes and folds of mud,
> it now is ...
>
> Amid the crushed red roses,
> Lay a cold body underneath a blanket
> Stained in blood.

Michael Deeley

Write a poem or description of the scene after an explosion. Write a contrasting description of the scene before the devastation.

IMAGINE YOU are a reporter assigned to this case. Write a newspaper article describing events and including statements from various people you have interviewed: neighbours, police, the injured. Make your headlines as dramatic and intriguing as possible.

IMAGINE THE BBC are making a documentary programme about the various mystery explosions. Write the introductory part of the script and one in-depth interview.

WRITE THE letter Mrs. Brady-Smith might have written to a friend describing the events on the day of the explosion.

THE POLICE wish to interview Peter Brady-Smith. Write the description of him they issue.

WRITE YOUR own story, play or poem entitled 'Trapped!'

WRITE A story or short play based on another incident involving the exploding paper.

M*etamorphosid Arkwright*

UNDERSTANDING THE PLAY

HARRY HAS strong views about women – 'You can't have lady members playing snooker' – and Albert about minority groups like 'skinheads and lefties'. What other examples of prejudice can you find in the play?

> *What has to be remembered about constructing a radio play is that the listener is very likely to be doing something else. The play must be constructed with this in mind, so that it is particularly absorbing and easy for the 'blind' listener to follow.*
> From *The Way To Write Radio Drama* by William Ash
> published by Elm Tree Books, London, 1985.

HOW FAR do you feel 'Metamorphosid Arkwright' succeeds in this respect?

WHAT SORT of research would the playwrights have undertaken before writing this play?

WHAT DO you learn about the relationship between Sid and his wife and son? In what ways does this relationship change as the play develops?

IDEAS FOR DISCUSSION AND IMPROVISATION

IN SMALL groups discuss the following statements made by some pupils and teachers who have read this play:

> *Comedy is the best way to learn the truth about ourselves and the play, although very funny, makes some serious and important points.*

> *The humour is too subtle, too Northern, young people will not be interested in this kind of drama.*

> *This is pure farce – hilarious, original, compelling.*

> *The depiction of the working men's club scene is highly exaggerated; it's not 'down all night, supping and playing darts and dominoes'.*

THE RADIO Script Editor often refers to a prepared list of questions a script reader should consider when recommending a play for acceptance. In groups look at a typical report sheet produced on the next page and apply the questions to 'Metamorphosid Arkwright'.

Report On Radio Drama

1 Is the story line interesting, original, absorbing, thought-pro-voking?

2 Are the characters realistic, powerful, well-drawn?

3 Is the dialogue believable, vivid, varied?

4 Will this play make good *radio*?

5 What would be the best time of day to broadcast this drama?

6 Is there a good sense of atmosphere and place?

7 Is the play about the right length? If not, can it be expanded or cut without artistic loss? Which parts could be cut or expanded?

8 How might this play be improved?
   – is the opening sufficiently compelling?
   – does the play end effectively?
   – is the cast too large?
   – is dramatic tension maintained?

9 What are the special problems with broadcasting this play? (For example, strong language, controversial themes, foreign settings, unusual sound effects.)

10 Is music required? If so, in what places and of what kind?

THE CLUB committee meets again to discuss whether or not to allow Eric's wedding reception to take place on the premises. Improvise the scene.

IMAGINE YOU are a reporter on 'The Westhorpe Chronicle' covering the amazing story of the Beetle-Man. Improvise the interviews with club members and Sid's wife and write the news report on this incredible story. Give your article an eye-catching headline.

IMAGINE SID rings The Samaritans asking for advice about his problem. In pairs simulate the call.

SID SAYS, 'I haven't been to 'doctors. I'm scared to.' Imagine Sid had sought medical advice. Improvise the scene between Sid and his doctor and write the doctor's report describing his patient's amazing change including any explanation for the condition and the treatment prescribed.

IN PAIRS improvise one of the following conversations:
– between Eric and Sharon, in which Eric tries to explain to his

fiancée why he has left home
- between Harry and his wife, in which Harry explains why the club committee suspended Sid's membership
- between El Magico and the secretary of another working men's club, in which the magician describes the events of the night when Sid crash-landed on the stage ruining his act.

IDEAS FOR WRITING

WRITE OUT the opening two scenes of the play as prose.

WHEN WE describe a person we often describe him or her by a short sentence, such as 'He's really mean' or 'She's always happy'. Describe in one sentence each of the main characters.

FRED IS the Westhorpe Working Men's Club Committee Secretary. Write the minutes he keeps for the meetings dramatised in the play.

DESCRIBE SID'S thoughts and feelings as he lay on his camp bed in the shed after Dora had evicted him.

WRITE YOUR own poem, story or play featuring a person like Sid as the main character who, because of some misfortune, loses his friends and his family.

'METAMORPHOSID ARKWRIGHT' is a parody, or comic imitation of a well-known short story called 'Metamorphosis' by Franz Kafka. Read the story and compare it with the play. Write your own parody of a short story you have read.

WHAT DO you imagine will happen to Sid in the next few years? Continue the play either as a story or a script.

THERE ARE many science fiction and supernatural stories and films about strange transformations, such as 'The Werewolf', 'The Incredible Shrinking Man', 'The Fly', 'Dr. Jekyll And Mr. Hyde'.
Write your own story about someone who undergoes an amazing and unexpected change.

EXTENDED STUDY ON DAUGHTERS AND SONS

A main theme of the collection is the relationship between young people and their parents. Very often it is the stressful and unhappy side of this relationship which is emphasised: the conflict and jealousy between Lisa and her stepmother in 'Home', the opposition and short-sightedness of Jackie's father in 'Keep On Running', Rachel's lack of understanding in 'Audition' and Eric's intolerance and lack of sympathy in 'Metamorphosid Arkwright'.

COMPARE THE way the different playwrights explore the relationship between parents and children.

WRITE ABOUT the duties and responsibilities of both parents and children. Below are three extracts which may give you ideas for your own writing.

1 *Guard against too much severity. By pursuing a steady course of efficient government, severity will very seldom be found necessary. If, when punishment is inflicted, it is done with composure and with solemnity, occasions for punishment will be very infrequent. Fear is a useful and a necessary principle in the government of children. God makes use of it in governing his creatures. But it is ruinous to the disposition of a child to control him exclusively by this motive. How unhappy, for example, must that family be, where the parent always sits, with a face deformed with scowls, and where the voice is always heard in tones of severity and command. But where kindness fails, and disobedience ensues, let not the mother hesitate for a moment to fall back upon her last resort, and punish as severely as is necessary. A few such cases will teach almost every child how much better it is to be obedient than disobedient.*

From *The Fourth Book of Lessons for the Use of Schools*,
Longman, Green and Company, 1862.

2 *If a woman and a man take on the role of parents then they must also take on the responsibilities which come with it. Looking in the papers today and seeing terrible reports on the television about baby battering and child abuse, it seems many parents are unsuitable for raising children. The first thing, of course, is to look after the physical needs of the child — food, clothes, somewhere to live. Then you have to show the child love and affection, protect and care for him or her. A parent shouldn't always be critical, comparing life when he was young or when she was a girl. Parents should support and encourage as best they can and take a real interest in their child's education. If they do all this then hitting the child will be unnecessary. I have never been slapped by my parents and I don't think I've turned out all that bad.*

From 'The Responsibilities Of Being A Parent',
an essay by Janet Wilson, aged 16.

3 *Children begin by loving their parents; after a time they judge them; rarely, if ever, do they forgive them.*

From 'A Woman Of No Importance'
by Oscar Wilde.

DESCRIBE THE ideal mother/father and daughter/son relationship.

DO YOU think that if and when you become a parent you will treat your children any differently from the way your parents treat you?

READ OTHER examples where poets, playwrights and novelists explore parent-child relationships.

WRITE ABOUT various writers' different experiences and perceptions. You might like to look at some of the following:

POEMS*

Father Says, Michael Rosen
The Son, Edward Lucie-Smith
I Love Me Mudder, Benjamin Zephaniah
Poem To My Daughter, Anne Stevenson
My Dad These Days, Philip Guard
Mother To Son, Langston Hughes
Ode To My Mother, Spike Milligan
You Brought Me Up, poem of the Uraon People, translated by W.C. Archer
Praise Song For My Mother, Grace Nichols

* Most of these poems appear in anthologies suggested in *Further Reading* on page 153.

SHORT STORIES

Tell Her Finny Says Hello, Moy McCrory, Sheba
Lucky Break, Brian Glanville, The Fiction Magazine
The Breadwinner, Leslie Halward
We Look After Our Own, Kath Walker, Heinemann
A Present For A Good Girl, Nadine Gordimer, Gollancz

NOVELS

The Coal House, Andrew Taylor, Collins
A Ragged Schooling, Robert Roberts, Fontana Collins
Isaac Campion, Janni Howker, Julia MacRae
The Witch's Daughter, Nina Bawden, Gollancz
A Flute In Mayferry Street, Eileen Dunlop, Richard Drew
It's My Life, Robert Leeson, Fontana Lions
The War Orphan, Rachel Anderson, Richard Drew

EXTENDED STUDY ON HOPES AND DREAMS

We all have hopes, dreams and aspirations.

Lisa in 'Home' longed for the day she could go to live with her father: 'It's all I ever wanted, to come back home to you.' Rachel in 'Audition' hopes to be cast as Abigail in the school play and this over-riding ambition makes her selfish and sometimes objectionable. Jackie dreams of becoming a champion runner but has to face many hurdles. Bert's dream becomes a nightmare when it turns into reality. Sid in 'Metamorphosid Arkwright' prays that he will return to his normal self.

WHAT ARE your dreams and aspirations?

HOW DO you imagine yourself to be in ten years' time?

LOOK AT examples in fiction and in poetry where the writers consider dreams and hopes. You may like to compare the following material:

POEMS*

The Drover's Dream, W. Tully
Anthem For Ireland, Desmond Leslie
From The Classroom Window, John Walsh
Imagine, John Lennon
Dream Variation, Langston Hughes
Where The Rainbow Ends, Richard Rive
In My Dreams, Kath Walker
There Runs A Dream, A.J. Seymour
Note For The Future, Jim Burns

* Most of these poems appear in anthologies suggested in *Further Reading* on page 153.

SHORT STORIES

First Kiss, Philip Callow
Broken Homes, William Trevor, Bodley Head
Nineteen Fifty-Five, Alice Walker, David Higham
Molly Morgan, John Steinbeck, Heinemann
He Wanted A Pear Tree, T.O. Beachcroft, Bodley Head

SPEECHES

I Have A Dream, Dr. Martin Luther-King, Longman

NOVELS

The Old Man And The Sea, Ernest Hemingway, Jonathan Cape
Of Mice And Men, John Steinbeck, Heinemann
A Little Love, Virginia Hamilton, Gollancz
Enter Tom, June Oldham, Puffin Plus
Pennington's Heir, K.M. Peyton, O.U.P.

Follow On
EXTENDED STUDY ON A WOMAN'S PLACE

All the plays in this collection consider, to a greater or lesser degree, experiences common to women and girls.

WHAT ARE the positions of women and girls in the society depicted by the playwrights?

DESCRIBE THE particular experiences of the female characters and consider how they are treated by fathers and boyfriends.

DO SOME research into the role of women and girls in society. You might like to start by thinking about:
– the images of men and women presented on the television, in newspapers and magazines
– the kind of language which reinforces the stereotyped view of men and women
– the depiction of women in literature. You may find it interesting to examine a selection of the available anthologies and novels and see how many are written by women, have strong female characters and involve men and women in non-traditional roles.

You may like to refer to some of the following material:

*POEMS**

Mama And Daughter, Langston Hughes
Poem For My Sister, Liz Lochhead
The Football Match, Julie Rowlands
Looking At Miss World, Grace Nichols
Warning, Jenny Joseph
Words Faile Me, The Women's Press

* Most of these poems appear in anthologies suggested in *Further Reading* on page 153.

SHORT STORIES

First Love, Melanie McFadyean, Virago
One Friday Morning, Langston Hughes, Harold Ober
Life Of Ma Parker, Katherine Mansfield, Constable
The Giant Woman, Joyce Carol Oates, Gollancz
Red Dress – 1946, Alice Munro, Penguin

NOVELS

A Proposal, Daisy Ashford
The Bluest Eye, Toni Morrison, Panther
Sumitra's Story, Rukshana Smith, Bodley Head

143

Daughters Of Passion, Julia O'Faolain, Penguin
Roll Of Thunder, Hear My Cry, Mildred Taylor, Penguin

AUTOBIOGRAPHIES

The Gilt And The Gingerbread, Anita Leslie, Hutchinson
A Story Half Told, Anita Leslie, Hutchinson

PLAYS

Motherland: West Indian Women to Britain in the 1950's, Elyse Dodgson,
    Heinemann
Plays By Women, M. Wander

EXTENDED STUDY ON FRIENDS

Friendship is a theme in several of the plays in this collection. Kim in 'Audition' and Mary and Glynnis in 'Keep On Running' show greater friendship to Rachel and to Jackie than Sid's so-called mates in 'Metamorphosid Arkwright'. In 'Home' Claire says, referring to Lisa, 'We can't be friends. It's not going to work that way.' Perhaps if Claire had been more of a friend, less of a stepmother, things wouldn't have turned out as they did.

COMPARE IN greater detail the way the different playwrights explore the relationship between friends.

WHAT DO you consider to be the qualities of a best friend? Is there something to be said for the view expressed by George Canning in 'New Morality':

> *Give me the avowed, erect and manly foe;*
> *Firm I can meet, perhaps return the blow;*
> *But of all plagues, good Heaven, thy wrath can send,*
> *Save me, oh, save me, from the candid friend.*

Also describe the kind of friend you can do without.

READ OTHER examples where poets, playwrights and novelists explore the theme of friendship.

WRITE ABOUT the different pictures of friendship which they describe. You may wish to look at some of the following:

*POEMS**

Oath Of Friendship, (First Century Chinese, translated by Kenneth Koch)
It Is A Puzzle, My Friend, Allan Ahlberg
Friends, Elizabeth Jennings
Poem: I Loved My Friend, Langston Hughes
Mart Was My Best Friend, Michael Rosen
First They Came, Pastor Niemoller
But O....., Adam Small
A Friend: To Claudia, Elizabeth Gurley Flynn

> * Most of these poems appear in anthologies suggested in *Further Reading* on page 153.

SHORT STORIES

How Anthony Made A Friend, Jan Mark, Kestrel
The Great Leapfrog Contest, William Saroyan, Faber and Faber

Stage Write

The Ceremony, Martyn Copus, Fontana Lions
Fozzy Foster And The Dreaded Cheek Wobbler, Gervase Phinn, O.U.P.
Country Lovers, Nadine Gordimer, Jonathan Cape
Games At Twilight, Anita Desai, Heinemann

PLAYS

If Only, David Cook, Longman (Imprint Series)
Manjit, Lakviar Singh, Longman (Imprint Series)
Good Neighbours, Leslie Stewart, Longman (Imprint Series)

NOVELS

Sweet Frannie, Susan Sallis, Puffin Plus
No Place Like, Gene Kemp, Puffin Plus
Hal, Jean MacGibbon, Puffin
Chase Me, Catch Nobody, Erik C. Haugaard, Granada
Friend Or Foe, Michael Morpurgo, Macmillan

Writing Your Own Play

Now you have read, discussed and acted out the plays in this collection, you may like to try writing your own one act drama. The following guidelines will help you:

PREPARATION

Ask yourself the following questions:
What is the play going to be about?
Where and when is it set? Will there be several different locations?
Is the play for the stage, television or radio?
What sort of audience is the play aimed at?
Are there any particular themes or issues you wish to explore?
How detailed will the stage directions/camera notes be?
Will there be humour, suspense, pathos, conflict, use of dialect?

IMPROVISATION

Some of the imagined situations described below are based on the major themes of this collection and can be used as a basis for improvisation and for scripted plays:

A teenage daughter brings home her latest boyfriend to meet her parents. The boyfriend is dressed outrageously, says very little and is several years older. In addition to the central characters, other parts might include a younger brother or sister, a grandparent, an interfering neighbour.

A teenage son is determined to prevent his parents from putting his grandfather into a home for the elderly. Additional characters in the play might be Grandfather's friend, Secretary of the British Legion, a social worker, a health visitor, the family doctor.

A boy or girl from a poor background dreams of becoming rich and successful. The chance comes with the offer of a job with a large importing firm. When the new employee discovers that the boss is involved in illegal activities, a choice has to be made: take a share of the profits or tell the police. Characters, in addition to the central ones, might include parents, friends and police officers.

On the eve of her marriage, a young woman discusses with her bridesmaids her hopes for a long and happy relationship with her husband to be. At his stag party the bridegroom tells his best man and friends what his expectations of married life are.

A woman employee in a firm of building contractors is passed over for promotion. The successful candidate is a man with less experience, fewer qualifications and a deserved reputation for laziness. She confronts her boss. Additional characters might include the manager's secretary, building workers, friends, a Trades Union Official, husband and family.

A close friend and one whom you have always trusted, betrays a confidence. You confront your friend in a crowded place. Additional characters might include parents, teachers and other friends.

During the improvisations you might use a 'freeze-frame' technique, where the action is stopped for actors and audience to explore aspects of the drama. This could take the form of a *full group discussion* in order to examine the situation and relationships and suggest a course of action and possible solutions. You might try *hot-seating*, where some of the characters are questioned about their activities and motives.

WRITING

The following guidelines might help when writing your play:

Make a rough outline plan of the play, devising the number of scenes and listing the characters.

What research is needed? For example, you may need information about the work of health visitors, Trades Union officials, local politicians, doctors, social workers and to be familiar with police procedures and the law concerning young people.

If the play is to be written for the stage, what kind of set and staging will be the most appropriate: the Proscenium Arch or 'traditional' stage, the arena stage (sometimes called 'theatre-in-the-round'), the thrust stage, the open stage or will it be a promenade performance?

If the play is intended for television or radio what special effects are required?

Write your first draft of the play. How detailed will the stage/recording/camera directions be?

Ask someone to read the play and make constructive criticisms and suggestions on how it might be improved. Redrafting may be necessary.

Write the final version.

Perform the play.

*W*riting *Your Own Review*

Before the final selection was made for *Stage Write* the plays were reviewed by teachers and students throughout the country. The response was varied. Which play did you enjoy the most? Which play did you like least? Would you read more plays by the writers represented in this collection?

If you wish to write a more detailed review, the following plan will offer some starting points:

SETTING

When and where is the play set?
Does the play create a particular atmosphere or mood?

TITLE

*I*s the title appropriate?
Can you think of a better title?

STORY

*H*ow does the play begin?
What are the central themes?
*A*re the events which take place ordinary, realistic, far-fetched or fantastic?
*D*o the scenes follow a linear pattern or are flashbacks/glimpses into the future used?
*H*ow does the play end? Is it cleverly contrived, unexpected, and is everything neatly explained or are you left guessing?

CHARACTERS

Who are the main characters?
What sort of people are they?
*A*re they convincing, interesting, rounded, true-to-life?
With which character do you most identify?
*I*s the playwright expressing his or her own opinions through any of the characters?

GENERAL

What part of the play remains most in your mind?
Does the play start you thinking in a fresh way about a particular issue or aspect of human behaviour?
*H*as the play influenced your attitudes about anything?
Does the play help you to understand aspects of the society in which we live?
Does the play make you feel sad, angry, bored, amused?
Would you recommend the play to other students?

Writing Your Own Poetry

As well as telling a story the playwrights in this collection make us think deeply about ideas and issues, which you may wish to respond to through poetry.

The following examples, all written by students, show the possible range of poetic responses to the main themes of the collection.

Dreams

Dirty little child with sticky nose,
Red-rimmed eyes and sparrow legs,
Empty belly and hand-me-down clothes,
And nothing his, save what he begs.
Maybe the Christian in us should see:
'**S**uffer little children to come to me.'

This student writes an *acrostic* on the word DREAMS, an interesting and demanding approach.

Friend

Oh, farewell false friend!
I shared with you my secrets,
Which you shared with all.

Here the student writes a *haiku*. This is based on a traditional Japanese poem following a fixed pattern of only three lines, the first of five syllables, the second of seven and the third line of five. The first line sets the scene, the second introduces some action and the last creates the relationship between the two.

This third poem is based on another Japanese verse form, the *tanka*. This gives a little more freedom for it consists of thirty-one syllables arranged in lines of 5, 7, 5, 7, 7.

Father Waiting

Down the silent street,
A father watches, waiting.
Face at window, still,
Rehearses the words he'll say
When daughter, with sun, appears.

One of the oldest forms of poetry is the *riddle*, or puzzle in words. A collection of Old English riddles is housed in the library at Exeter Cathedral and dates back to the eleventh century. In the following riddle one idea is suggested but the answer is rather different.

I come to you at dead of night,
When all is darkness, still,
Prodding, probing, a flashing kaleidoscope of memories.
At times I slide like a silent snake around your brain,
Then jump and bite like a terrier with a rat —
Worrying.
And you awake gaping, gasping, sweat-covered and afraid.

The answer to this riddle is Nightmare.

In this free verse poem the writer has thought carefully about the words he uses and the arrangement. The poem was written shortly after the Heysel Football Stadium disaster in Belgium.

Back Home

Giovacchino Landini was flown home today
On a morning white hot and still.
His coffin, black and cold,
Was placed in the hold of an Italian Airforce plane.
His wife and daughter grieve for him, raw and open,
And huddle together weeping.

Andrea Casula was flown home today,
On a warm, dark night, scented with Japonica.
His small coffin, draped in colour,
Lay by his father's.
He was ten and loved football.

In this poem the writer uses rhyme and rhythm to good effect:

Mum And Dad

Eighteen, army, Ireland, fight, against his mother's will.
Father's bursting proud and loud, kill son or be killed.
Pity, sorrow, gentle touch, missing mother's caress.
Struggle, strife, need for life, act under duress.
Cold and nervous, wet with tears, frightened and alone.
Blood and bullets, sweat and death, bitter to the bone.
Holiday, seaside, Blackpool pier, laughter, sand and sun,
Mother gave him kisses, Dad a toy gun.

Try writing your own poems. They may be acrostics or riddles, haikus or tankas, free verse or rhymed. The following guidelines offer some starting points:

Think about the idea for your poem: an experience, a person, a scene, a particular issue, a mood.

Write down any words, images, phrases which you hope to develop. Do not be concerned at this stage with such formal considerations as rhyme and rhythm.

151

Write a first draft. It will at this stage lack structure and coherence but there will be certain phrases, perhaps a line or two, which will appear in the final version.

Start to order your poem. Redraft if necessary.

Let someone else read your poem and give suggestions on how he or she feels it could be improved.

Write out your final version.

Further Reading

Home

BERLIE DOHERTY

Berlie Doherty is a highly acclaimed writer of vivid and compelling stories and plays. She worked as a children's social worker and as a teacher before concentrating on full-time writing. Many of her very varied stories and plays have been broadcast on BBC Radio Four and two of her children's novels have been read on BBC Television.

Four of her novels – The Making Of Fingers Finnigan, Children Of Winter, White Peak Farm *and* How Green You Are *– have been published by Fontana and her novel* Granny Is A Buffer Girl *won The Carnegie Award, 1987.*

Her latest novel, Tough Luck, *published by Hamish Hamilton, and written as the result of a term she spent as writer-in-residence at a Doncaster comprehensive school, is a fast moving, uncompromising and realistic story well worth reading.*

PROSE

Sweet And Sour, edited by Gervase Phinn, Unwin Hyman Short Stories
Summer's End, Archie Hill, Wheaton – novel
Your Friend Rebecca, Linda Hoy, Bodley Head – novel
Other Days Around Me, Florence McDowell, Blackstuff Press – novel

PLAYS

Still Waters, Julie Jones, Longman (Imprint Series)
Radio Plays, Henry Reed, BBC Publications
Worth A Hearing – 5 Radio Plays, Blackie and Son
Separate Tracks, Jane Rogers, Fontana
A Sense Of Shame, Jan Needle, Fontana
Pearl, A Radio Play, John Arden, Methuen

POEMS

Talking Blues, Centerprise
New Ships, D.G. Wilson, O.U.P.
Strictly Private, edited by Roger McGough, Kestrel Books

CRITICAL READING

The Art Of Radio, Donald McWhinnie, Faber and Faber
The Way To Write Radio Drama, William Ash, Elm Tree Books

Replay For A Plumber

GERARD MELIA

Gerard Melia taught in a variety of schools before becoming a school inspector at Newham. He is a prolific writer of stories, plays and poems all of which have a genuine and fresh approach, clear and lively language and an astute social observation.

He has three novels published by Hodder and Stoughton – Green Strawberry, Britannia Rules OK and Nurse – and two publications in the Longman Knockout Series – his play Will Of Iron and novel Silvertown Disaster.

PROSE

Supernature, Lyall Watson, Coronet – research into the supernatural

Mysteries, Colin Wilson, Hodder and Stoughton – reference book

Strange Powers, Colin Wilson, Abacus – informative anecdotes

Ed McBain's Mystery Book, Kirby McCauley Ltd – prose collection

The Methuen Book Of Strange Tales and *The Methuen Book Of Sinister Stories*, edited by Jean Russell, Methuen – short stories

Tales Of Mystery And Imagination, Edgar Allen Poe, Longman – short stories

The Shadow Cage, Philippa Pearce, Puffin – ten supernatural tales

The Ghost Of Gritstone Grange And Other Stories, Gervase Phinn, Arnold-Wheaton (Story Chest Series)

PLAYS

The Weathermonger, Jan Mark, Longman (Star Plays Series)

Sound Scene, Alfred Bradley, Longman (Imprint Series)

Six Plays For Radio, Giles Cooper, BBC Publications

POEMS

Poems, edited by Michael Harrison and Christopher Stuart-Clark, O.U.P.

New Collected Poems, Vernon Scannell, Robson Books

Poetry 1900–1975, edited by George Macbeth, Longman (English Series)

Bluefoot Traveller, James Berry, Harrap

*K*eep On Running

ROGER BURFORD-MASON

Roger Burford-Mason was born in Norfolk in 1943 but now lives in Hertfordshire with his wife and teenage son.

He has written extensively for BBC Schools Radio and several of his stories have been broadcast on Radio Three and Four. His latest play, 'Schoolboy Snooker Star' appears in the recently published Race To Be Seen *(Longman Imprint Books).*

He is a keen jazz musician and cricketer.

PROSE

The Village By The Sea, Anita Desai, Heinemann New Windmill – novel

Wild Saturday And Other Stories, Joyce Carol Oates, Dent Everyman – short stories

The Stories Of Raymond Carver, Raymond Carver, Picador – short stories

The Experience Of Sport, edited by John L. Foster, Longman (Imprint Series) – prose and poetry collection

Shooting Star, Michael Hardcastle, Fontana – novel

PLAYS

Dash And Defiance, edited by Alison Leake, Longman (Imprint Series) – three plays

Radio Plays, Don Haworth, BBC Publications

The Best Radio Plays Of 1982, Methuen

Conflicting Generations, edited by Michael Marland, Longman

POEMS

Consider These Poems, edited by Alan Proud, Edward Arnold

Changing Islands, chosen by Eric Boagey, Unwin Hyman

Close Relatives, Vicki Feaver, Martin Secker and Warburg

Choice, Richard Murphy, Goldsmith Press

CRITICAL READING

Calling All Playmakers, Maisie Cobby, Pitman

Leap Of Life, John Wiles and Alan Garrard, Chatto and Windus

*A*udition

ALMA CULLEN

Alma Cullen is a distinguished playwright and her many and varied plays rank her amongst the very best writers for television. Her first television drama, 'The Caledonian Cascade' was snapped up by Granada Television and presented as the first in the autumn season of Sunday Night Plays in 1977. Since then Alma Cullen has written a range of powerful and original dramas: 'A Hardy Breed Of Girl' (Granada), 'Kay' (BBC), 'A Degree Of Uncertainty' (BBC Play for Today), 'Lives Of Our Own' (Granada). In 1982, her STV play 'Northern Lights' was shortlisted for an Emmy Award and another STV play, 'Two Per Cent', won the Pharic MacLaren Award in the same year. Her most recent film, 'Off Peak' (STV), won the Silver medal at the 1984 New York Television Festival.

Alma Cullen lives in Edinburgh with her husband and two teenage children.

PROSE

The Gamecock And Other Stories, Michael McLaverty, Jonathan Cape – short stories

Johnny Jarvis, Nigel Williams, Puffin – novel

Love Stories, Harry Gilbert, Longman (Knockout Series) – short stories

Meetings And Partings, edited by Michael Marland, Longman (Imprint Series) – short stories

The Penguin Dorothy Parker, Dorothy Parker, Penguin – writings, letters and articles

You Can't Keep A Good Woman Down, Alice Walker, Women's Press – short stories

That'll Be The Day, edited by Roy Blatchford, Unwin Hyman Short Stories

PLAYS

The Crucible, Arthur Miller

Gregory's Girl, Bill Forsyth, C.U.P. (Act Now Series)

Roots, Rules And Tribulations, Andrew Bethell, C.U.P. (Act Now Series)

Frankly Frankie, Rony Robinson, Macmillan (Dramascript Series)

Identities, edited by Gill Goldenburg and Steve Goldenberg, Thames Television Publications

POEMS

Selected Poems, Langston Hughes, Hughes Massie Ltd

Hot Dog And Other Poems, Kit Wright, Kestrel Books

Into Poetry, Richard Andrews, Ward Lock

Poetry Workshop, Michael and Peter Benton, Hodder and Stoughton

CRITICAL READING

Performance Skills In Drama, Rosemary Linnell, Edward Arnold

The Way To Write For Television, Eric Paice, Elm Tree Books

*M*etamorphosid Arkwright

IAN MCMILLAN/JOHN TURNER

Ian McMillan is perhaps better known for his poetry rather than for his plays. His volume Selected Poems *was a Poetry Society Recommendation and many of the poems which appear in his seven published collections he 'performs' in a highly original and entertaining way. He is a member of a dynamic comedy team called The Circus of Poets, a four-part rhythm and rhyme group which tours schools, colleges and clubs. He was recently the presenter of the Channel 4 programme 'Write On'. He has recently completed a year as writer-in-residence at Sheffield City Polytechnic.*

John Turner is also a member of The Circus of Poets which have appeared at the Edinburgh Festival. He is a poet, playwright and video commentary scriptwriter who, like Ian McMillan, is a regular visitor to schools and colleges.

PROSE

Metamorphosis And Other Stories, Franz Kafka, Penguin Books – short stories

Hundred More Stories, O. Henry, Hutchinson – short stories

Life With Father, Clarence Day, Hutchinson – novel

The Thurber Carnival, James Thurber, Penguin – short stories

Life Among The Savages, Shirley Jackson, Brandt and Brandt – four short biographies

The Harrap Book Of Humorous Prose, edited by Michael Davis, Harrap – short stories and extracts

PLAYS

Mummy's Boy, Gervase Phinn, Arnold-Wheaton (Story Chest Series)

Laughter And Fear, David Campton, Blackie

Perci And Other Plays, Gervase Phinn, Longman (Star Plays Series)

Six Silly Plays, Paul Groves, Longman (Star Plays Series)

Playbill One, Two And Three, Alan Durband, Hutchinson

POEMS

Salford Road, Gareth Owen, Kestrel Books

The Well Wishers, Edward Lucie-Smith, O.U.P.

No Fool Like An Old Fool, Gavin Ewart, Gollancz

CRITICAL READING

Writing For The BBC, BBC Publications

*A*cknowledgements

The editor and publishers would like to express thanks to the following for permission to reproduce plays included in this anthology:

'Home' © Berlie Doherty.

'Keep on Running' © Roger Burford-Mason.

Audition © Alma Cullen, c/o Sheila Lemon of agents Lemon & Durbridge Ltd, London.

'Replay For A Plumber' © Gerard Melia.

'Metamorphosid Arkwright' © John Turner and Ian McMillan.